Nations
in Focus

Written by Sandy Sturmer
Published by Prim-Ed Publishing

Researching Cultural, Geographical and Historical Data of Nations of our World

Nations in Focus is a copymaster for upper primary which contains ten sets of research and activity pages.
Each set has four pages - allowing the student to collate an overview of ten different nations or continents.
The activities in each set focus on a specific nation or country and provide the pupils with a complete nation's profile when their data is collected.

Within each set of activities the following information may be researched:

Geographical Information: landforms, climate and oceans.
National Customs: dress, foods, ceremonies and festivals.
Culture: lifestyle, transport, clothing, sports and religion.
Current Information: population, currency, language, government, sights to see and capital cities.
History: famous people, historical data and special days.
Native Flora and Fauna: wildlife, environmental problems and endangered species.

Other information may be researched depending on the nation under review.
The pupils will be encouraged to use a variety of resources including:

- local and school libraries;
- embassies;
- computer information retrieval systems;
- encyclopaedias;
- resource books and atlases; and
- magazines, newspapers, cookbooks and travel brochures.

Teachers may use the set of activities in a variety of ways:

- Research and information retrieval activities in the school library or classroom.
- Project starters - as a catalyst to stimulate a more detailed project using the headings given in the activities.
- Multicultural stimulus - to initiate a multicultural theme in the classroom.
- Homework activity - as a homework assignment.

The ten nations or countries have been chosen because they represent a diversity in culture, history and geography.

Contents

CHINA

About China

China is one of the __ __ __ __ __ __ civilisations

in the __ __ __ __ __.

With over one billion __ __ __ __ __ __, it has

a larger __ __ __ __ __ __ __ __ __

than any other __ __ __ __ __ __ __.

The name China comes from the Chin people (or Qin)

who founded China's first __ __ __ __ __ __ in 221 BC.

China's Flag

*Draw and colour
the design of
China's national
flag below.*

Geographical Features

*Use your atlas to locate and place
the following on your map.*

1. Plateau of Tibet
2. Yangtze River
3. Yellow Sea
4. South China Sea
5. Himalayas
6. Huang He River
7. Tropic of Cancer
8. Gobi Desert
9. Guangzhou
10. Manchuria
11. Bayan Har Mountains
12. Red Basin
13. Urumqi
14. Beijing
15. Lanzhou
16. Shanghai

China was the first country to
cultivate roses and
chrysanthemums.

➡ *Write a report on one
of these flowers.*

*What is the
'Willow Pattern'?*

Where in the world is China? Colour it!

China's Neighbours

The country of China borders on 14 countries. Name them!

_____

_____

_____

_____

_____

_____

_____

_____

_____

_____

_____

This building is the _____ in _____.

CHINA

Information Search *Find the following facts about China.*

Population: _____

Currency: _____

Language(s) spoken: _____

Capital city: _____

Type of government: _____

Leader's title: _____

Religious beliefs: _____

Popular sports and pastimes: _____

This is an

a _ _ _ _ _.
It is the ancient way of
calculating numbers
used by the Chinese.

History of China

Find the answers to the following questions.

1. Who built the Great Wall of China?
2. Why was it built?
3. Was it successful?
4. What is the Terracotta Army?
5. Who was Marco Polo and what did he achieve?
6. Who was Confucius?
7. What did he believe was important?
8. What can you find out about the Dalai Lama?

| 551 BC |
| 221-206 BC |
| 202 BC-AD 220 |
| AD 581-618 |
| AD 618-907 |
| AD 960-1279 |
| AD 1279-1368 |
| AD 1368-1644 |
| AD 1644-1912 |
| AD 1920s |

Write the dates from the timeline next to the correct historical event.

- Ming Dynasty _____
- Sui Dynasty _____
- Birth of Confucius _____
- Mongols invade, and set up Yuan Dynasty _____
- Communist Party formed _____
- Song Dynasty _____
- Chin (or Qin) people formed the first empire _____
- Han Dynasty _____
- Tang Dynasty develops cultures _____
- Manchurians invade, and set up Qing Dynasty _____

Chinese Inventions

Use the clues given to find one of China's most important inventions.

Clue 1: Used to find direction - N S E W.
Clue 2: A one-wheeled cart for carrying loads.
Clue 3: Used as the explosive for guns, fireworks and weapons.
Clue 4: Devices which can fly in the sky attached to long strings.
Clue 5: A fine form of China made into vases and dishes.

What is a Dynasty?
What is Communism?

The answer is: _ _ _ _ _ _

➠ *Find out how it is made.*
➠ *What is it made from?*
➠ *Describe the process.*
➠ *How is it used?*

Even More Inventions!

The Chinese were responsible for many other inventions. Can you unjumble them?

dreudr - _____ kswifroer - _____ kils - _____ blaelmur - _____ nugs - _____

➠ *Choose one of these inventions and write a report on the impact that it has had on society today.*

Chinese Foods
Use the words on the noodles to complete the passage about foods.

Noodle words: woks, bean, chopsticks, cheese, shoots, north, rice, bowls, scarce, noodles, soya, dairy, baskets, tea, steamed

In the _____ of China, people tend to eat _____ with their meals, and in the south people tend to eat _____. Meat is _____ and many vegetables are eaten such as bamboo _____, _____ sprouts and _____ beans. The food is mostly _____ or fried. It is steamed in _____ and fried in metal pans called _____. _____ is the most common drink. The food is served in small _____ and eaten using _____. Most Chinese do not like eating _____ products such as _____ or milk.

Foods grown in the north.

_____
_____
_____
_____

Foods grown in the south.

_____
_____
_____
_____
_____

Regional Recipes
Find a recipe which uses a particular food from these regions:
Canton, Sichuan, Peking and Shanghai.

Calligraphy and Language
There is no alphabet in the Chinese language. Instead, each word or syllable is symbolised by a character or shape which has its own meaning.
There are about 50 000 characters!
Calligraphy is done with brush and ink.
➡ *Try writing these words.*

人 man　大 big
口 mouth　天 sky
木 tree　头 head
雨 rain　众 crowd

Traditional Dress

- *Join the correct tops with the correct bottoms.*
- *Copy or trace each of these traditional dress styles.*
- *Colour them.*

Animals of China
China's most famous animal is the giant p _ _ _ _. It is the symbol for the W _ _ _ _ _ W _ _ _ _ Fund for N _ _ _ _ _ _. Pandas eat only one special variety of b _ _ _ _ _. Other animals found in China are the s _ b _ _ _ _ an tiger, d _ _ _ and m _ _ _ k _ _ _ s. Birds of China include _ _ _ a _ _ _ _, p _ _ c _ _ _ k _ and the M _ _ _ _ _ _ _ _ duck.
➡ *Write a detailed report on one of China's animals. Include: description, habitat, foods and enemies.*

Name China's main exports.

Exports

_____
_____
_____
_____

Trade in China - Exports and Imports
Highlight the key words in this passage.

China is a land of great mineral wealth, such as oil and coal. Silk and cotton are two of the natural fibres which are processed in China. Textiles are important for export, as well as for the people. Japan is China's main trading partner. New technology and more machinery have increased the amount of products available for trade.

Name China's main imports.

Imports

_____
_____
_____
_____

Yin and Yang
This symbol shows the balance of the Yin and Yang.
Find the characteristics of:

Chinese Festivals
China celebrates many traditional festivals.
- Chinese New Year
- Qing Ming Festival
- Moon Festival
- Dragon Boat Festival

Find out the following for two of these festivals.
1. When is it celebrated?
2. What does the festival celebrate?
3. How is it celebrated?
4. Who celebrates?

The Yellow River
Answer the following.
1. What is the Chinese name for the Yellow River? _____
   _____
2. Why is it called the Yellow River? _____
   _____
3. What is the name of the Chinese boat below?
   _____
4. What are these boats used for?
   _____
5. What shape is the bottom of the boat?
   _____

Yin	Yang

Dragon Puppet
- *Colour the dragon head in bright colours.*
- *Stitch coloured wool to the dragon's chin to make a fiery beard.*
- *Glue or stitch your dragon head onto the toe end of a long sock.*
- *Put your hand into the end of the sock to bring your dragon to life!*

AFRICA

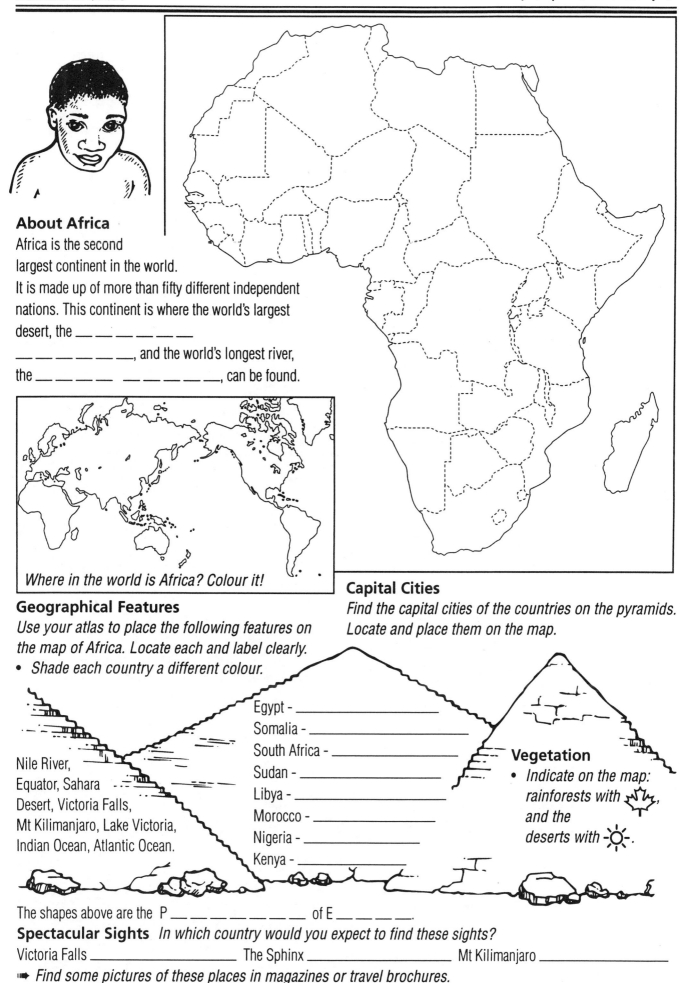

About Africa

Africa is the second
largest continent in the world.
It is made up of more than fifty different independent
nations. This continent is where the world's largest
desert, the __ __ __ __ __ __
__ __ __ __ __ __ __, and the world's longest river,
the __ __ __ __ __ __ __ __ __ __, can be found.

Where in the world is Africa? Colour it!

Geographical Features

*Use your atlas to place the following features on
the map of Africa. Locate each and label clearly.*
• *Shade each country a different colour.*

Nile River,
Equator, Sahara
Desert, Victoria Falls,
Mt Kilimanjaro, Lake Victoria,
Indian Ocean, Atlantic Ocean.

Capital Cities

*Find the capital cities of the countries on the pyramids.
Locate and place them on the map.*

Egypt - _____
Somalia - _____
South Africa - _____
Sudan - _____
Libya - _____
Morocco - _____
Nigeria - _____
Kenya - _____

Vegetation
• *Indicate on the map:
rainforests with ☙,
and the
deserts with ☼.*

The shapes above are the P __ __ __ __ __ __ __ __ of E __ __ __ __.

Spectacular Sights *In which country would you expect to find these sights?*

Victoria Falls _____ The Sphinx _____ Mt Kilimanjaro _____

➠ *Find some pictures of these places in magazines or travel brochures.*

Information Search *Find the following facts about one African nation.*

Population: _____

Currencies: _____

Main language(s) spoken: _____

Religious beliefs: _____

Popular sports and pastimes: _____

The People of Africa

Highlight the key words in the passage.

There are many different races in Africa. With more than fifty different independent countries using various languages, currencies and lifestyles, the variety within the racial groups in Africa is wide. The races can be classified into five main racial groups:

- *Africans* - The black Africans account for more than 70 per cent of the total population. They include the Zulus, Pygmies, Hottentots and Masai tribes and were probably the original inhabitants of Africa.
- *Asians* - People of the island of Madagascar migrated from Indonesia more than 2 000 years ago.
- *Europeans* - Europeans from Britain, Holland and France settled in parts of Africa from the 1600s onwards.
- *Indians* - Indians migrated from India to Africa in the 1800s and settled in southern and eastern Africa.
- *Arabs and Berbers* - Arabs settled in Africa as early as the 600s. Most live in Egypt. Berbers live mainly in Algeria and Morocco.

The Differences Between Races

List some differences between a Masai warrior and a Saudi Arabian.

Physical Appearance: _____   Physical Appearance: _____

_____   _____

Dress: _____   Dress: _____

_____   _____

Foods: _____   Foods: _____

Housing: _____   Housing: _____

_____   _____

Transport Used: _____   Transport Used: _____

_____   _____

Language: _____   Language: _____

_____   _____

Religion: _____   Religion: _____

_____   _____

Wild Animals of Africa

Many people go to Africa to see the animals roaming free on the Savannah. Africa has thousands of species of birds, mammals, reptiles and insects. As the environment is changed or destroyed, many of the animals are in danger of becoming extinct.

O	R	E	L	A	K	C	A	J	U	G
C	H	E	E	T	A	H	M	A	N	O
R	I	Z	A	N	E	Y	H	A	G	R
O	N	N	O	A	G	V	P	N	A	I
C	O	A	K	H	I	E	I	D	Z	L
O	C	P	A	P	R	M	S	G	E	L
D	E	M	P	E	A	T	B	S	L	A
I	R	I	I	L	F	R	N	I	L	E
L	O	H	F	E	F	A	O	B	E	A
E	S	C	Z	H	E	N	D	I	M	L

Can you find the sixteen animals hidden in the sleuth?

c _ _ _ _ _ _ _   g _ _ _ _ _ _ _   r _ _ _ _ _ _ _ _ _ _ _ _

e _ _ _ _ _ _ _ _   o _ _ _ _ _   j _ _ _ _ _ _

l _ _ _ _   i _ _ _ _   a _ _ _   c _ _ _ _ _ _ _ _ _

g _ _   g _ _ _ _ _ _ _   f _ _ _ _ _ _ _ _ _

c _ _ _ _ _ _ _ _ _ _   h _ _ _ _   g _ _ _ _ _ _

Choose one African animal and complete the cloze.

My animal is the _____. It lives in _____.

It eats _____ and its enemies are _____

_____. It protects itself by _____.

Its colours are _____. Its young are called _____

African Foods   *Unjumble the words in brackets.*

Most _____ (lraru) families have to grow _____ (dofo) crops

for their survival; however, the _____ (olis) is very poor due to overuse.

They _____ (peke) chickens and perhaps _____ (togas)

or sheep. Food crops grown include _____ (**eatpuns**), millet and maize

in _____ (redri) areas, and _____ (**eric**), **bananas**

and _____ (toor) **vegetables** in the wetter areas.

In _____ (tonrh) Africa, a dish called couscous

is _____ (mnomco).

It is made from steamed grains, _____ (gbltavesee) and meat.

The dish is eaten with _____ (tfal) breads made

from _____ (singar).

Crops such as _____ (feecof), fruits, **cocoa beans** and

_____ (**tocuncos**) are grown to _____ (lesl).

➡ *Design a healthy meal which might be eaten by the rural families in Africa.*

➡ *Find recipes which contain the foods in bold print.*

AFRICA

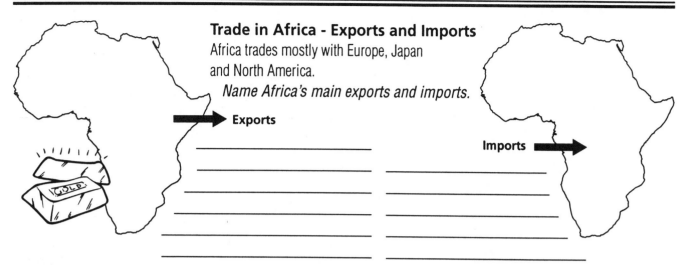

Trade in Africa - Exports and Imports
Africa trades mostly with Europe, Japan and North America.

Name Africa's main exports and imports.

Exports

_____
_____
_____
_____
_____

Imports

_____
_____
_____
_____
_____

Problems in Africa
Africa has many serious problems. Some of these are poverty and food shortages brought on by droughts and poor soil, and illiteracy due to little education. Disease and poor nutrition lead to sickness.

Find out about:

Somalia - _____
_____

Apartheid - _____
_____

Rwanda - _____
_____

Nelson Mandela - _____

Traditions and Customs of Africa
Many of the rural African tribes still wear colourful beads, necklaces, earrings and bracelets as part of their daily clothing.

• *Colour the mask on the left in as many colours as you might imagine an African tribal leader may do to prepare for a special ceremony.*

Jewellery Design
Design any piece of jewellery you wish, using gold, diamonds, emeralds and colourful beads.

RUSSIAN FEDERATION

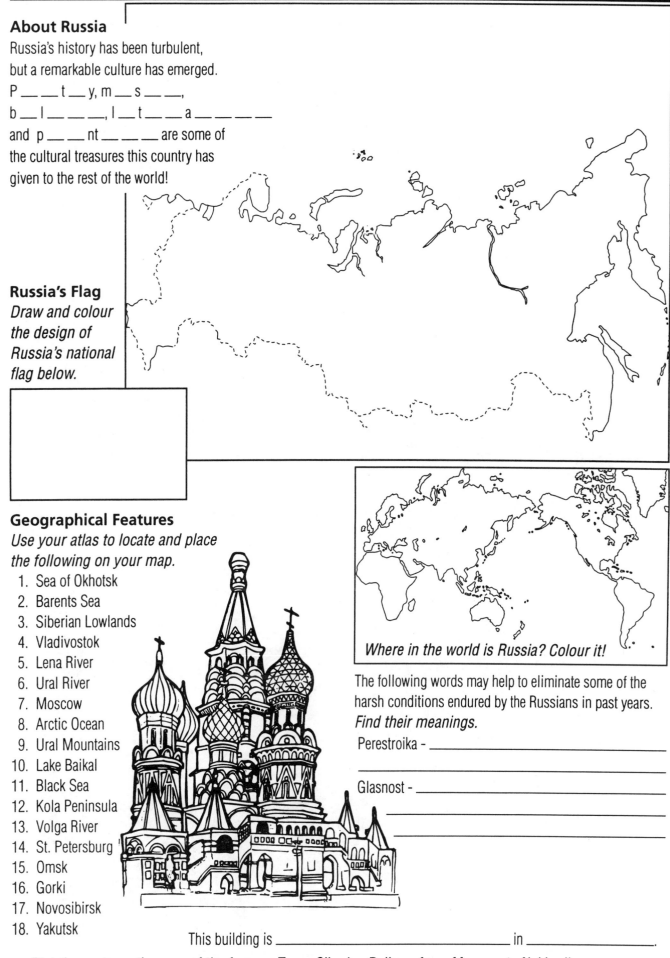

About Russia

Russia's history has been turbulent,
but a remarkable culture has emerged.

P __ __ t __ y, m __ s __ __,

b __ l __ __ __ __, l __ t __ __ a __ __ __ __

and p __ __ nt __ __ __ are some of
the cultural treasures this country has
given to the rest of the world!

Russia's Flag

*Draw and colour
the design of
Russia's national
flag below.*

Geographical Features

*Use your atlas to locate and place
the following on your map.*

1. Sea of Okhotsk
2. Barents Sea
3. Siberian Lowlands
4. Vladivostok
5. Lena River
6. Ural River
7. Moscow
8. Arctic Ocean
9. Ural Mountains
10. Lake Baikal
11. Black Sea
12. Kola Peninsula
13. Volga River
14. St. Petersburg
15. Omsk
16. Gorki
17. Novosibirsk
18. Yakutsk

Where in the world is Russia? Colour it!

The following words may help to eliminate some of the
harsh conditions endured by the Russians in past years.
Find their meanings.

Perestroika - _____

_____

Glasnost - _____

_____

_____

This building is _____ in _____.

➠ *Plot the route on the map of the famous Trans-Siberian Railway from Moscow to Nakhodka.*

Nations in Focus

RUSSIAN FEDERATION

Information Search *Find the following facts about Russia.*
Population: _____
Currency: _____
Main language(s) spoken: _____
Capital city: _____
Type of government: _____
Leader's title: _____
Religious beliefs: _____
Popular sports and pastimes: _____

This is a picture of
P _ _ _ _ _ the
G _ _ _ _ _.

History of Russia
Match the dates given with the following events which have occurred during Russia's turbulent history.

The Bolshevik Party, led by Vladimir Lenin, seized power. _____

Peter the Great ruled, and encouraged Russians to become more industrial and cultural. _____

The USSR disintegrated into 15 independent countries and Russia is led by Boris Yeltsin.
_____

Joseph Stalin ruled Russia. _____

Mikhail Gorbachev becomes the leader of the Communist Party. _____

The first Russian Tsar was Ivan the Terrible. He was very cruel and introduced serfdom. _____

The formation of USSR - the Union of Soviet Socialist Republics.
_____

Catherine the Great was German, but ruled Russia for 34 years. _____

1547 - 1584	1985
1991	1682 - 1725
1924 - 1953	1922
1917	1762 - 1796

This building is the _____ in _____. Now it is called the
_____ _____. It was the winter residence of the Russian Tsars.

The Russian Language
The Russian language is the official language spoken throughout Russia.
However, there are more than 160 other languages spoken.
The Russian alphabet is called _____.
It was named after St Cyril, a Greek missionary to Russia
in the _____ century.

Can you write these words in Russian?
My name is _____
I live in _____
I eat _____ and _____.
I like to wear _____

А Б В Г Д Е Ё   Ж З И Й К Л М   Н О П Р С Т У   Ф Х Ц Ч Ш Щ Ъ   Ы Ь Э Ю Я

RUSSIAN FEDERATION

Famous Russians

Complete the table below by filling in the name, event or achievement which has been important to the Russian people. Who did what?

My Name	Achievement or Event
Anna Pavlova	_____
_____	I was the first human in space, I orbited the earth on 12 April 1961.
_____	I won the Nobel Prize in 1965 for my novels and stories.
Anton Chekhov	_____
Grigori Rasputin	_____
_____	I won three Olympic Gold Medals for gymnastics in 1972.
Rudolph Nureyev	_____
Alexander Solzhenitsyn	_____
_____	Musical composer: The Nutcracker and Swan Lake.
Leo Tolstoy	_____

➡ *Choose one of these people and prepare a two-minute talk about him/her to present to the class.*

Traditional Russian Clothing

Russia is a land of climatic contrasts and the clothing worn by its people differs greatly: from the Turks, who are desert dwellers, to the Siberians who live in ice and snow. *Draw a picture of a Turk, a Siberian and a Cossack in the boxes.*

Turk	Siberian	Cossack

Animals of Russia

What is Russia's national symbol? Find the answer by unjumbling the letters given in the clues below. Each clue is an animal or bird found in Russia.

Clue 1: First letter in wolf.
Clue 2: Sixth letter in sparrow.
Clue 3: Second letter in grouse.
Clue 4: First letter in butterflies.
Clue 5: Fifth letter in hedgehog.
Clue 6: Second letter in crow.
Clue 7: Sixth letter in polar bear.
Clue 8: Second letter in hare.
Clue 9: Fourth letter in reindeer.

About the National Symbol
➡ *Research: types of; its habitat; foods; description; enemies; and hibernation.*

The letters are __ __ __ __ __ __ __ __ __ and the answer is __ __ __ __ __ __ __ __ __ .

RUSSIAN FEDERATION

Nations in Focus

Industry in Russia *Read the following information about industry in Russia, and highlight the key words.*
Before 1991, The Soviet Union owned all factories and farms. These did not run efficiently and there were many food and supply shortages.
Since 1991, new government has begun to improve conditions by allowing foreign businesses to buy into Russia. Russia has some of the richest reserves of coal, oil and natural gas. Mineral reserves of gold, copper, iron ore and precious stones are found in the local mountains. The southern regions produce wheat, barley and maize.
Factories produce machinery, tractors and heavy vehicles. Although Russia's economic situation is low at present, it will improve because of its vast natural resources, and a huge labour force who are willing and able to work.

Russian Foods *Describe the following Russian foods on the Shashlik Stick.*

➡ *What are these?*
Caviar - _____
_____
Samovar - _____
_____
Beef Stroganov - _____
_____

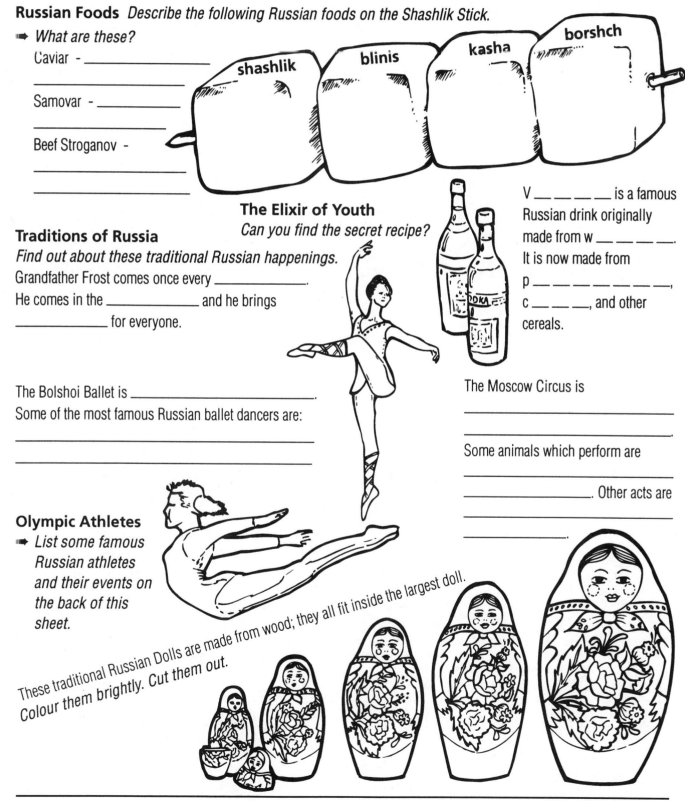

shashlik   blinis   kasha   borshch

The Elixir of Youth
Can you find the secret recipe?

V __ __ __ __ is a famous Russian drink originally made from w __ __ __ __. It is now made from p __ __ __ __ __ __ __, c __ __ __, and other cereals.

Traditions of Russia
Find out about these traditional Russian happenings.
Grandfather Frost comes once every _____.
He comes in the _____ and he brings _____ for everyone.

The Bolshoi Ballet is _____.
Some of the most famous Russian ballet dancers are:
_____
_____

The Moscow Circus is
_____
_____
Some animals which perform are
_____
_____. Other acts are
_____
_____

Olympic Athletes
➡ *List some famous Russian athletes and their events on the back of this sheet.*

These traditional Russian Dolls are made from wood; they all fit inside the largest doll. Colour them brightly. Cut them out.

Prim-Ed Publishing - 12

INDIA

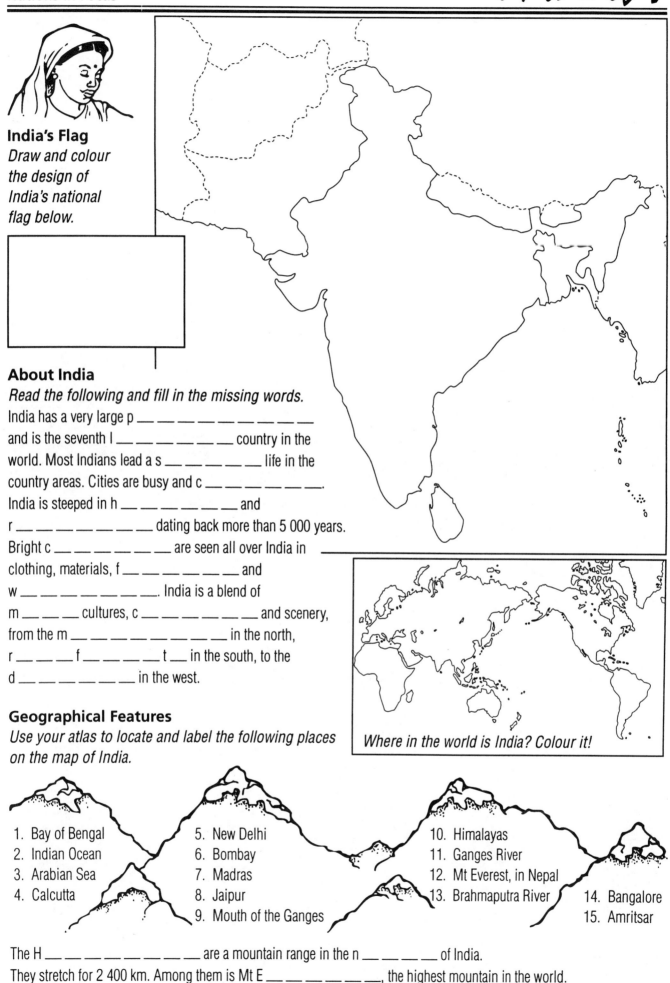

India's Flag

Draw and colour the design of India's national flag below.

About India

Read the following and fill in the missing words.

India has a very large p __ __ __ __ __ __ __ __ __ __ and is the seventh l __ __ __ __ __ __ country in the world. Most Indians lead a s __ __ __ __ __ life in the country areas. Cities are busy and c __ __ __ __ __ __ __.

India is steeped in h __ __ __ __ __ __ and r __ __ __ __ __ __ __ __ dating back more than 5 000 years.

Bright c __ __ __ __ __ __ are seen all over India in clothing, materials, f __ __ __ __ __ __ and w __ __ __ __ __ __ __. India is a blend of m __ __ __ cultures, c __ __ __ __ __ __ __ and scenery, from the m __ __ __ __ __ __ __ __ __ in the north, r __ __ __ f __ __ __ __ __ t __ in the south, to the d __ __ __ __ __ __ __ in the west.

Geographical Features

Use your atlas to locate and label the following places on the map of India.

Where in the world is India? Colour it!

1. Bay of Bengal
2. Indian Ocean
3. Arabian Sea
4. Calcutta
5. New Delhi
6. Bombay
7. Madras
8. Jaipur
9. Mouth of the Ganges
10. Himalayas
11. Ganges River
12. Mt Everest, in Nepal
13. Brahmaputra River
14. Bangalore
15. Amritsar

The H __ __ __ __ __ __ __ __ __ are a mountain range in the n __ __ __ __ __ of India. They stretch for 2 400 km. Among them is Mt E __ __ __ __ __ __ __, the highest mountain in the world.

INDIA

Information Search *Find the following facts about India.*

Population: _____

Currency: _____

Language(s) spoken: _____

Capital city: _____

Type of government: _____

Leader's title: _____

Religious beliefs: _____

Popular sports and pastimes: _____

Religion in India

Hindu people treat animals with great respect. They believe the cow is sacred as it is a symbol of man's identity with life. Most are vegetarians because they don't believe in killing animals for food.

The Ganges River

Hindu people believe the Ganges River is sacred. They come to the Holy River to bathe. However, this sacred river is becoming very polluted.

Solve these problems.

1. What other meats may be eaten by the Hindus?
   _____

2. When people are bathing in the sacred Ganges River, how can they avoid becoming sick from the pollution? _____
   _____

3. What can be done to stop the pollution, and to clean up the pollution, in the Ganges? _____
   _____
   _____

The Taj Mahal

One of the most beautiful buildings in the world is the Taj Mahal. It was built by the emperor Shah Jahan in memory of his wife, Mumtaz Mahal, who died in 1632. It took 21 years to build.

Fill in these six key pieces of information.

Name of the building: _____ Built by: _____

Reason: _____

When building started: _____ When finished: _____ It is now _____ years old.

➠ *Cut around the outline of the Taj Mahal. Fold along the dotted lines to make your 3-D model.*

INDIA

Clothing in India All Indians do not dress the same. In different country areas, the dress is more traditional.
• *Colour the different styles of dress below. What is a: sari?* _____

dhoti? _____
turban? _____
lunghi? _____

Indian Foods and Drink
Use resource books and encyclopaedias to find the answers to the following.

1. What grain is grown and eaten with meals in the south? _____
2. What meats are forbidden to be eaten for religious reasons? _____
3. Name four spices commonly used in Indian foods. _____
   _____   _____   _____

• *Colour the dish of food.*

4. What is the name of the flat bread eaten with meals in the north? _____
5. Special underground ovens are called _____.
6. True or false: Indian meals are mostly vegetarian. _____
7. More tea is drunk in the _____, and coffee is drunk in the _____.
8. Most Indians do not use a _____ and _____ to eat their food.
   Explain how they eat their food. _____
   _____
9. Which hand is used to eat food with in India? _____
10. Find a recipe which contains spices, rice and vegetables. Copy it onto the back of this page.

What are these foods?
samosa, pappadums, dhal and korma

Animals and Birds of India *Find the Indian wildlife by unjumbling these words.*

aclofn	ryeg wfol	mealcs
acokpce	gerti	fubfloa
nikg bocar	gamfilon	rabes
der napad	csoorihenr	draploe
kemoyn	nateeplh	

➡ *Find this information about tigers and peacocks.*
1. Habitat and camouflage.
2. Foods and prey.
3. Enemies.
4. Colourings and description.
5. Location - where seen.

➡ *What are the two main differences between the Indian elephant and African elephant?*

Endangered Wildlife
➡ *Write a report on an endangered species. Include: name, picture of the animal, three reasons for becoming endangered, what is being done to prevent extinction, and suggestions to prevent extinction.*

INDIA

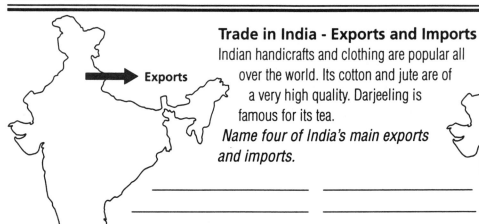

Trade in India - Exports and Imports

Indian handicrafts and clothing are popular all over the world. Its cotton and jute are of a very high quality. Darjeeling is famous for its tea.

Name four of India's main exports and imports.

Exports

Imports

_____   _____

_____   _____

_____   _____

_____   _____

Transport in India

India has one of the largest rail systems in the world. Its large population uses the railway as its main form of transport.

Name other forms of transport used in the city and country areas of India.

City areas   Country areas

_____   _____

_____   _____

_____   _____

Craft in Camouflage

• *Colour the picture. Find the tigers and peacock.*

Temples and Shrines

The majority of Indians are Hindus. The picture (left) shows a temple in southern India at Madurai. It is covered with elaborate carvings.

• *Use a block of soap and carefully carve your name onto it. (Be careful.)*

• *Imagine what it is like to carve in stone.*

This is the Golden Temple in Amritsar.

➡ *Find information about this temple: location, religion, features, when it was built and by whom.*

MEXICO

About Mexico

The official name for Mexico is
the U _ _ _ _ _ _
M _ _ _ _ _ _
S _ _ _ _ _. Scenery can
change from deserts to tropical rainforests.
This country is rich in history and culture.

Mexico's Flag

*Draw and colour
the design of
Mexico's national
flag below.*
The main colours
are _____
_____.

Geographical Features

*Use your atlas to locate and
place the following on your map.*

1. Gulf of Mexico
2. Pacific Ocean
3. Gulf of California
4. Acapulco
5. Mexico City
6. Chihuahua
7. Yucatan Peninsula
8. Bay of Campeche
9. Guadalajara
10. Monterrey
11. Tijuana
12. Sierra Madre
13. Mt Citlaltepetl
14. Rio Grande River
15. Sonora Desert
16. Neighbouring countries:
    USA, Guatemala, Belize

This Monarch Butterfly migrates
from North America and
Canada to spend Winter in the forests of Central Mexico.
What are its colours? _____
_____

*Name three other migrating birds or
animals.* _____
_____
_____
_____

Where in the world is Mexico? Colour it!

Spectacular Sights

This is the _____ at Chichen Itza.

➡ *Write down, on the back of this sheet, why Acapulco, the Yucatan Peninsula and Popocatepetl Volcano
are spectacular places to visit. Find some pictures of them.*

MEXICO

Information Search *Find the following facts about Mexico.*

Population: _____

Currency: _____

Language(s) spoken: _____

Capital city: _____

Type of government: _____

Leader's title: _____

Religious beliefs: _____

Popular sports and pastimes: _____

This is a

c _ _ _ _ _ _

p _ _ _ _ _!

History of Mexico *Write the dates from the timeline next to the correct historical event.*

1821-1824

1929-1934

AD 250

1863

Mid 1300s

1846-1848

1519-1521

- Great Indian civilisations thrived in the Valley of Mexico. _____
- The USA defeated Mexico in the Mexican War and won much of the Mexican territory. _____
- French troops occupied Mexico City. _____
- Mexico won independence and became a republic. _____
- Hernándo Cortés conquered the Aztec Empire for Spain. _____
- Aztecs founded Tenochtitlan, which is now Mexico City. _____
- The National Revolutionary Party was formed and land was given to farmers. _____

➠ *The Aztec Empire was very powerful. Find out some information about the empire, and why it was so powerful.*

The Yucatan Peninsula

Highlight the key words in the following passage.
The Mayan Indians settled in the Yucatan Peninsula and great civilisations began to develop. Huge, flat-topped pyramids were built on the limestone plateaus of the peninsula at Palenque. The Toltec Indians conquered the Mayans in about AD 950. They built and sculpted huge, carved warriors from rock. These warriors can still be seen today at Tula.

➠ *Plot the two cities mentioned on your map of Mexico.*
➠ *Write a report on the Mayans, Toltecs or Aztecs.*
➠ *Find pictures of the temples, palaces and tombs built by these people.*

MEXICO

Mexican Foods

Mexican food is very healthy because the beans provide fibre, and the fruit and vegetables provide vitamins. It is often very spicy. Chilli powder is even sprinkled on fresh fruit salad! Chocolate is added to a sauce for turkey dinner.

Find the words by spiralling outwards from the centre.

Can you find the twenty food and drink words hidden in the taco?

_____
_____
_____
_____
_____
_____
_____
_____
_____
_____
_____
_____

Describe the following foods.

Tortilla - _____

Biscochos - _____

Guacamole - _____

➡ *Make up a menu using traditional Mexican food and drink.*
   Don't forget to include the ingredients. How it is served? A diagram?

➡ *Find out about tequila. What is it made from? Where is it made? The traditional way to drink it? Variations - Mezcal?*

Flora and Fauna of Mexico *Use the words below to complete the information passages.*

monkey	painful	Grey	lizard	orchids	born	milk	weigh	damp	scales
warm	loudest	rocky	rain	monster	water	forests	cactus	roots	

1. Mexico is famous for its wild _____.
   These flowers like warm, _____
   conditions to grow.

2. Mexico has more types of _____ than any other
   country. Its swollen stems hold _____ for long
   periods. Shallow _____ absorb any
   _____ that falls.

3. The _____ whale is one of
   Mexico's famous animals. The babies are
   _____ in the _____
   waters off Baja, California. Babies
   _____ half a tonne, and drink 200
   litres of _____.

4. The _____ on the left is a Gila
   _____. It is one of only two
   poisonous lizards in the world. It has
   rounded _____, and
   its bite is very
   _____. It lives
   in the _____ areas.

5. This Mexican black
   howler _____
   can make one of the
   _____ noises
   of any animal. This
   monkey lives in the
   _____ and
   grasslands of Yucatan.

MEXICO

Trade in Mexico - Exports and Imports

Mexico mines many products. Silver is one of the country's largest mining products.
Mexico also produces z _ _ _, l _ _ _ _ and c _ _ _ _ _ _.
Name Mexico's main exports and imports.

Exports
_____
_____
_____
_____
_____
_____

Imports

Tourism is increasing, and huge reserves of oil have been discovered recently.
Name three products made from silver. _____

Clothing in Mexico

Most Mexicans wear western-style clothing, but traditional clothing is worn for festivals and celebrations. The colours worn are bright, and the patterns are intricate.

A sombrero - _____
_____

A poncho - _____
_____

• *Cut out the pieces of clothing and glue together to make a Huichol Indian in traditional clothing.*

Aztec Design *Make an Aztec shield.*

Mexican Festivals

Mexico has many festivals. Popular ways to celebrate festivals include rodeos, firework displays, parades and dancing.
Find out what these Mexican traditions are, and how they relate to festivals.

Fiesta - _____
_____
_____

Pinata - _____
_____
_____

Siesta - _____
_____
_____

• *Cut out this shield and glue onto stiff card.*
• *Colour brightly. Place feathers around the shield.*
➡ *Design a warrior's headdress to match your shield.*

JAPAN

Climate in Japan

Fill in the missing letters to find out about the Japanese climate.

Japan has very distinct seasons of the year.

The Winters in the n __ __ __ __ are long, c __ __ __ and icy.

The S __ __ __ __ __ __ in the south are hot and

h __ __ __ __. Typhoons are a d __ __ __ __ __ __ in

September because they bring strong w __ __ __ __ and flooding

r __ __ __ __. S __ __ __ __ __ is a beautiful season because

all the cherry blossoms are in flower.

Japan's Flag

Draw and colour the design of Japan's national flag below.

Its colours are _____ and _____.

Geographical Features

Use your atlas to locate and place the following on your map.

1. Name the four main islands of Japan.

   _____ _____

   _____ _____

2. The capital city - _____

3. Nearest neighbours:

   N __ __ __ __ K __ __ __ __ __

   S __ __ __ __ K __ __ __ __

   R __ __ __ __

   C __ __ __ __

Where in the world is Japan? Colour it!

12. North Pacific Ocean
13. Sea of Japan
14. Korea Strait
15. Mt Fuji
16. Inland Sea
17. Kitakami River

City on the Island of:

4. Sapporo on _____
5. Kobe on _____
6. Kagoshima on _____
7. Hiroshima on _____
8. Wakkanai on _____
9. Kyoto on _____
10. Yokohama on _____
11. Osaka on _____

This is Mt F __ __ __, the highest mountain in Japan. Its height is _____ m.

JAPAN

Information Search *Find the following facts about Japan.*

Population: _____

Currency: _____

Language(s) spoken: _____

Capital city: _____

Type of government: _____

Leader's title: _____

Religious beliefs: _____

Popular sports and pastimes: _____

This says Ei-go which means 'English language'. *Can you copy these letters?*

Calligraphy and Language

The Japanese started borrowing writing characters from China in about AD 500 to form their own writing. The Chinese characters are based on pictures to form words. Japanese children have to learn at least 2 000 of these characters, called 'kanji'. Some of the Chinese characters were simplified into symbols which represent sounds in the language. The most common of this group is 'hiragana', which is more rounded, and the other is 'katakana', which is square shaped. These three groups of characters form the Japanese writing. Traditional Japanese writing is written in columns from top to bottom and from right to left on the page. *Write down two differences between Japanese and your writing.*

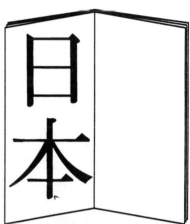

This says Ni-hon which is the Japanese name for Japan. 'Ni' means Sun, and 'Hon' means Source - 'Land of the Rising Sun'. *Can you copy these letters?*

Japanese Foods

Use the words inside the rice bowl to fill the spaces in the passage.

raw   sushi   snack   fish   rice   fresh
Japanese   famous   seaweed

Traditional _____ cooking consists mainly of _____, fish and vegetables. Fish is often eaten _____, and must therefore be very _____.

One of Japan's most _____ dishes is sashimi, which is raw _____. Another popular dish is _____ which is raw fish wrapped in _____.

Noodles are a favourite _____.

Japanese Chopsticks

Chopsticks are used instead of knives and forks.

They can be made of ivory or wood.

Chopsticks would be _____ (more or less) difficult for me to use

because _____

_____

➡ *Find a recipe using rice. Write it on the back of this sheet.*

About Japan *Write the names of two of the main islands, by finding the clues to the words across.*

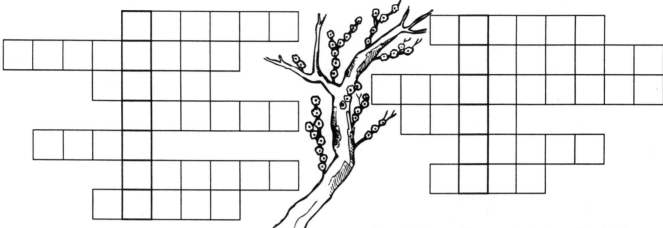

Clue 1: A place of worship for Japanese.
Clue 2: One of the main religions in Japan.
Clue 3: This grain is one of the main foods in Japan.
Clue 4: The traditional Japanese costume.
Clue 5: A traditional sport practised by the samurai.
Clue 6: A self-defence sport in Japan.
Clue 7: This dish is raw fish, rice and seaweed.

This island is _____.

Clue 1: This tree blossoms in Spring with pink flowers.
Clue 2: The art of paper folding.
Clue 3: The Japanese name for the 'Bullet Train'.
Clue 4: This food must be eaten fresh.
Clue 5: A Japanese poem using seventeen syllables.
Clue 6: This wrestling is performed by large men.

This island is _____.

Japanese Festivals
Highlight the key words in the passage below which tells you about some of Japan's festivals.
The New Year festival, called Shogatsu, is the biggest festival of the year and the most important. People gather at the local shrine to celebrate. Everyone has a holiday. Girls' Festival is celebrated on 3 March. Dolls are dressed in ancient costumes and displayed on red velvet. On 5 May, Children's Day is celebrated. Families with sons fly paper carp (fish), as large as kites, from their houses.

The Bon Festival in August is the Japanese 'Halloween'.
In spring, Japanese families gather under the cherry trees to have a picnic under the blossoms.
The Snow Festival is held in Sapporo. Visitors come to see the huge statues made from ice.
➡ *Make a list of the festivals that you celebrate.*

This is a cherry tree without blossoms in Winter.

- *Roll small pieces of pink tissue paper and glue them onto the branches.*
- *You will have a cherry tree in blossom, in Spring.*

JAPAN

Trade in Japan - Exports and Imports

Because Japan is a small country with a large population, the amount of space to grow its food is limited. Therefore, some of its foods need to be imported. Japan also imports large amounts of iron ore. This enables it to produce and export many products. *Name some of Japan's main exports and imports.*

Exports ←

Imports →

Some well-known Japanese brand names of electronic equipment or cars are:

```
T _ Y _ _ A      H _ _ D _
N _ _ S _ N      S _ _ _ Y
P _ N _ _ O _ _ C
M _ Z _ _ _      H _ _ _ A C _ I
```

Japanese Words

Can you find out what the following Japanese words mean?

Samurai - _____

Tatami - _____

Kabuki - _____

Sake - _____

Traditional Dress

This is a kimono, which is the traditional dress worn by both men and women. Generally, it is made of silk. There is a wide sash worn around the middle, called an obi. Nowadays, they are only worn on special occasions.

• *Design your own pattern on the kimono to the right.*

Haiku

Japanese poets began to write poems called haiku in the 17th century.

Each poem has only 17 syllables, arranged in three lines of 5 - 7 - 5 syllables.

➡ *Try writing you own haiku poem on the butterfly. Colour the butterfly in bright colours and patterns.*

BRAZIL

About Brazil
Brazil began to develop in the 15th century, when the P _ _ _ _ _ _ _ _ _ _ _ _ claimed the country as a colony. The native I _ _ _ _ _ _ _ tried unsuccessfully to defend their land. Negro slaves were brought from W _ _ _ A _ _ _ _ _ to work on the sugar cane plantations. This vast country is now a colourful mixture of these races; and the Brazilians have a love of music, dance and carnivals.

Brazil's Name
How did Brazil get its name?_____
_____
_____
_____
_____

Brazil's Flag
Draw and colour the design of Brazil's national flag below.
Its colours are
_____
_____.

Geographical Features
Use your atlas to locate and place the following on your map.

1. Amazon River
2. Equator
3. Rio de Janeiro
4. São Paulo
5. Brazilian Highlands
6. Manaus
7. Macapá
8. Atlantic Ocean
9. Salvador
10. Belém
11. Recife
12. Brasilia
13. Pôrto Alegre
14. Marajo Island
15. Mouths of the Amazon River

This building is the _____ of _____ Cathedral in _____.

Where in the world is Brazil? Colour it!

Brazil's Neighbours
Brazil has ten neighbouring countries. Name them!

_____ _____
_____ _____
_____ _____
_____ _____
_____ _____

B·R·A·Z·I·L

Information Search *Find the following facts about Brazil.*

Population: _____

Currency: _____

Language(s) spoken: _____

Capital city: _____

Type of government: _____

Leader's title: _____

Religious beliefs: _____

Popular sports and pastimes: _____

This is a statue of C _ _ _ _ _ _ overlooking the city of R _ _ _ _ J _ _ _ _ _ _.

The Amazon

The word Amazon conjures up pictures of dense tropical rainforests, untamed animals and tribes of forest Indians.   *To complete a mini-project on this fascinating part of the world, use the following headings as a guide.*

1. Source, location and size of the Amazon.
2. Rivers and tributaries.
3. Climate of the Amazon.
4. Unique animals of the Amazon jungles.
5. Lifestyle of the peoples of the Amazon.
6. Destruction of the rainforests, its effects on the environment and global warming - solutions.
7. Products of the rainforest.
8. Hydroelectric dam on the T   ocantins River .
9. The canopy .

➡ *You may choose to present your project in a booklet, on a chart or as a class talk.*

Brazilian Products

Find out about these products.

Coffee Beans
Research the process involved from the coffee bean to the drink.

Timber
1. What are the main trees?
2. What products are made?

Cacao Beans
1. What product is made from the cacao bean?

_____

2. What is the process?

_____

_____

Brazil Nut
Name other fruits and nuts grown in Brazil.

_____

_____

_____

The Rubber Tree
What is the process of extracting rubber from the tree?

_____

_____

_____

What is made from the rubber?

_____

_____

BRAZIL

Wildlife of Brazil
Unjumble the names of the wildlife found in the rainforests of Brazil. Hurry - before the piranhas eat them!

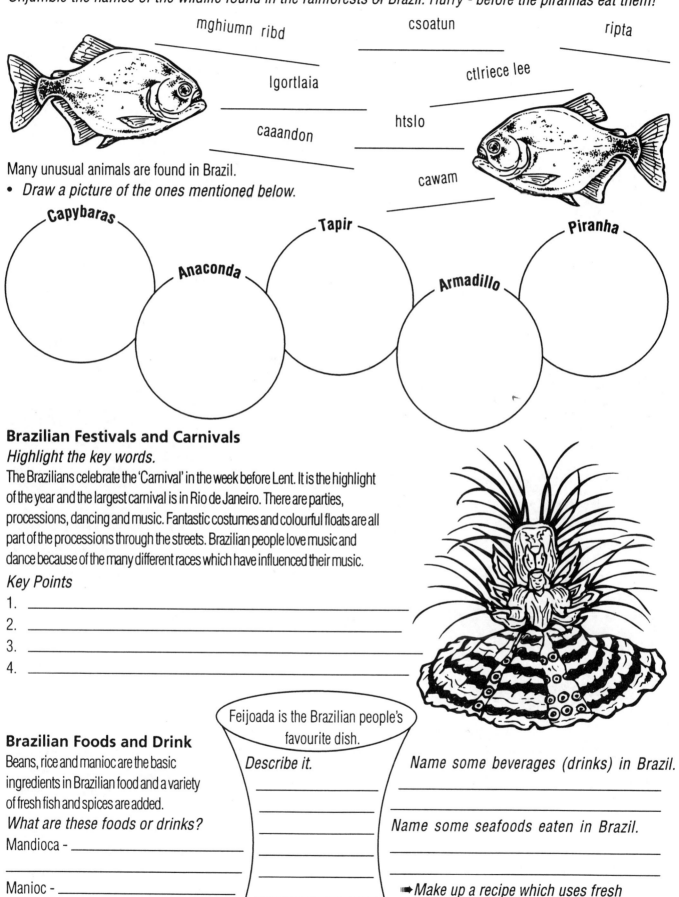

mghiumn ribd

csoatun

ripta

lgortlaia

ctlriece lee

htslo

caaandon

cawam

Many unusual animals are found in Brazil.
• *Draw a picture of the ones mentioned below.*

Capybaras

Anaconda

Tapir

Armadillo

Piranha

Brazilian Festivals and Carnivals
Highlight the key words.

The Brazilians celebrate the 'Carnival' in the week before Lent. It is the highlight of the year and the largest carnival is in Rio de Janeiro. There are parties, processions, dancing and music. Fantastic costumes and colourful floats are all part of the processions through the streets. Brazilian people love music and dance because of the many different races which have influenced their music.

Key Points

1. _____
2. _____
3. _____
4. _____

Brazilian Foods and Drink
Beans, rice and manioc are the basic ingredients in Brazilian food and a variety of fresh fish and spices are added.

What are these foods or drinks?

Mandioca - _____
_____

Manioc - _____
_____

Feijoada is the Brazilian people's favourite dish.

Describe it.
_____
_____
_____
_____
_____
_____

Name some beverages (drinks) in Brazil.
_____

Name some seafoods eaten in Brazil.
_____

➡ *Make up a recipe which uses fresh fruits and nuts found in Brazil.*

B·R·A·Z·I·L

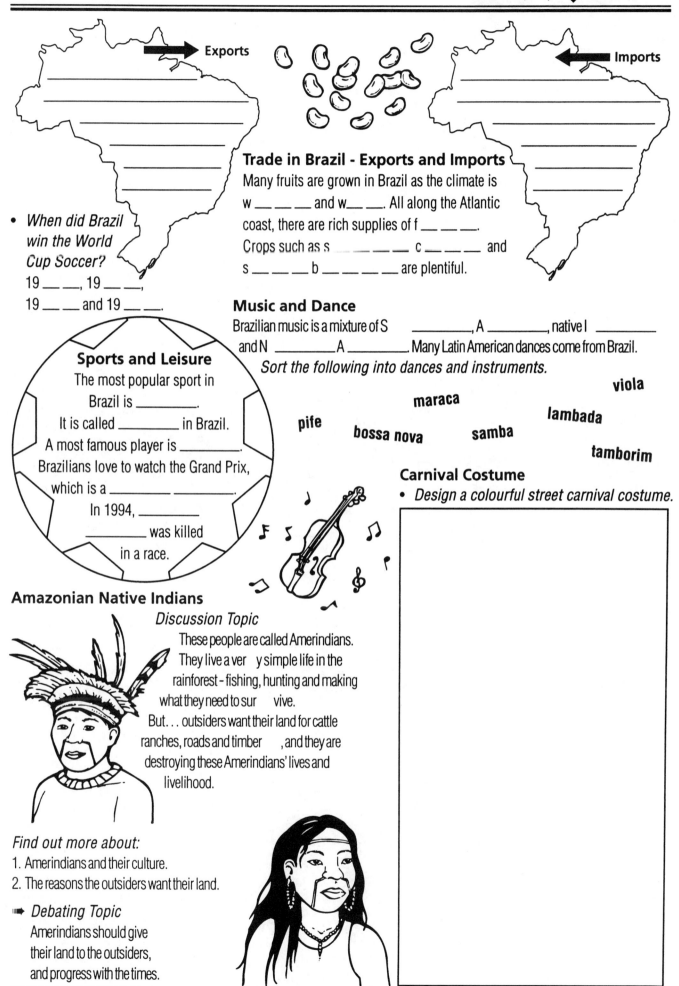

Exports

Imports

- *When did Brazil win the World Cup Soccer?*
19 __ __, 19 __ __, 19 __ __ and 19 __ __.

Trade in Brazil - Exports and Imports
Many fruits are grown in Brazil as the climate is
w __ __ __ and w__ __. All along the Atlantic
coast, there are rich supplies of f __ __ __.
Crops such as s __ __ __ __ c __ __ __ and
s __ __ __ b __ __ __ __ __ are plentiful.

Music and Dance
Brazilian music is a mixture of S _____, A _____, native I _____
and N _____ A _____. Many Latin American dances come from Brazil.
Sort the following into dances and instruments.

maraca

pife

bossa nova

samba

viola

lambada

tamborim

Sports and Leisure
The most popular sport in
Brazil is _____.
It is called _____ in Brazil.
A most famous player is _____.
Brazilians love to watch the Grand Prix,
which is a _____ _____.
In 1994, _____
_____ was killed
in a race.

Carnival Costume
- *Design a colourful street carnival costume.*

Amazonian Native Indians

Discussion Topic
These people are called Amerindians.
They live a ver y simple life in the
rainforest - fishing, hunting and making
what they need to sur vive.
But… outsiders want their land for cattle
ranches, roads and timber , and they are
destroying these Amerindians' lives and
livelihood.

Find out more about:
1. Amerindians and their culture.
2. The reasons the outsiders want their land.

➡ *Debating Topic*
Amerindians should give
their land to the outsiders,
and progress with the times.

THAILAND

About Thailand

The Thai people consider it courtesy not to laugh heartily. However, they capture many hearts with their charm and ability to smile. Thailand is sometimes called the 'L __ __ __ of S __ __ __ __ __ __,' or 'L __ __ __ of the F__ __ __!'

Thailand's Flag

Draw and colour the design of Thailand's national flag below.
The main colours are _____
_____

Geographical Features

Use your atlas to locate and place the following on your map.

1. Gulf of Thailand
2. Ubon Ratchathani
3. Bangkok
4. Andaman Sea
5. Chao Phraya River
6. Ping River
7. Ayutthaya
8. Wang River
9. Phuket
10. Chiang Mai
11. Nan River
12. Burma (Myanmar)
13. Laos
14. Malaysia
15. Tanen Markets
16. Cambodia

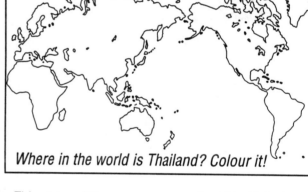

Where in the world is Thailand? Colour it!

This statue of B __ __ __ __ __ is at Wat Mahathat. It is one of the many temples in B __ __ __ __ __ __.

Buddha, Buddhism and Buddhist Temples

There are more than 300 temples in Thailand, and several million images of Buddha!

1. Who is Buddha? _____
2. How did Buddhism evolve? _____
   _____
3. What are the Buddhist beliefs? _____
   _____

➡ *Name and draw one of the more famous temples.*

THAILAND

Information Search *Find the following facts about Thailand.*

Population: _____

Currency: _____

Language(s) spoken: _____

Capital city: _____

Type of government: _____

Leader's title: _____

Religious beliefs: _____

Popular sports and pastimes: _____

History of Thailand

Research the following information.

1. King Ramkamhaeng w   as also known as

   _____.

   He ruled in _____ until _____.

2. Name some of the good reforms brought about in
   Thailand. _____

   _____

3. The Kingdom and City of Ayutthaya was

   established by the _____

   River. The city was destroyed by

   _____ and the capital city is now

   _____.

4. In 1782, this nation had the name of _____. In the year _____ the name of the
   countr y was officially changed to Thailand.

Seasons in Thailand

Thailand is considered to have only three
seasons.   What are they?

1. _____

2. _____

3. _____

Transport throughout Thailand

Answer the following questions about transport in Thailand.

1. What is the name of the main river running through Thailand? _____

2. Its canals are called _____.

3. In busy cities, what are the main forms of transport? _____

4. What are the main forms of transport in rural areas? _____

5. On what side of the road do the drivers in cars drive? _____

6. How many international airports are in Thailand? _____

7. Can you name this form of Thai transport? _____

8. Draw the design
   of the Thai Airways
   in the box.

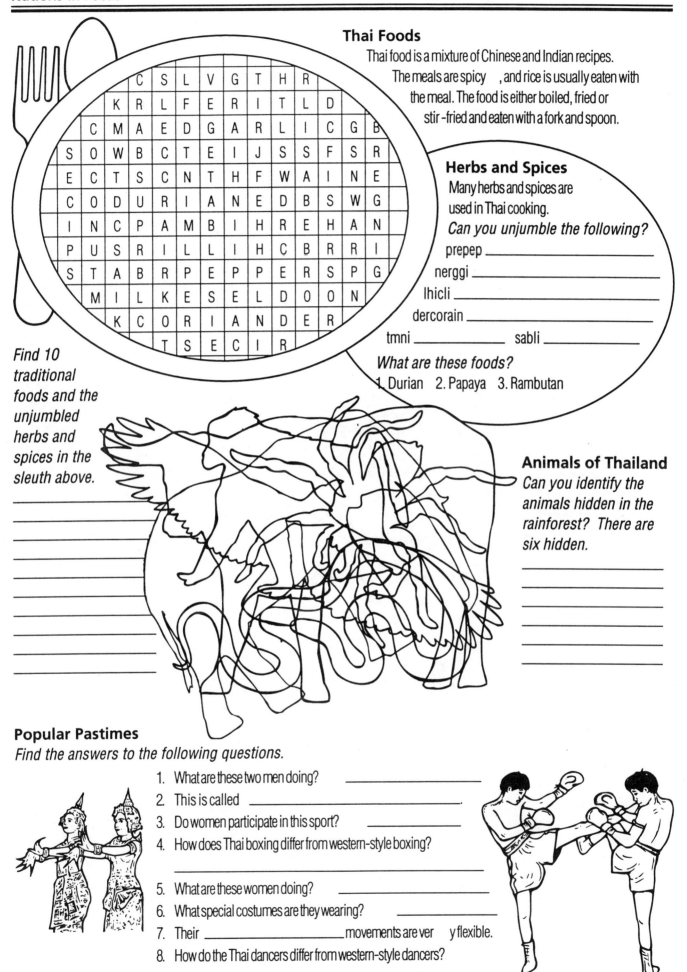

Thai Foods

Thai food is a mixture of Chinese and Indian recipes. The meals are spicy , and rice is usually eaten with the meal. The food is either boiled, fried or stir-fried and eaten with a fork and spoon.

	C	S	L	V	G	T		H	R		
	K	R	L	F	E	R	I	T	L	D	
C	M	A	E	D	G	A	R	L	I	C	G	B
S	O	W	B	C	T	E	I	J	S	S	F	S	R
E	C	T	S	C	N	T	H	F	W	A	I	N	E
C	O	D	U	R	I	A	N	E	D	B	S	W	G
I	N	C	P	A	M	B	I	H	R	E	H	A	N
P	U	S	R	I	L	L	I	H	C	B	R	R	I
S	T	A	B	R	P	E	P	P	E	R	S	P	G
M	I	L	K	E	S	E	L	D	O	O	N
	K	C	O	R	I	A	N	D	E	R
		T	S	E	C	I	R

Find 10 traditional foods and the unjumbled herbs and spices in the sleuth above.

_____
_____
_____
_____
_____
_____
_____
_____

Herbs and Spices

Many herbs and spices are used in Thai cooking.

Can you unjumble the following?

prepep _____

nerggi _____

lhicli _____

dercorain _____

tmni _____ sabli _____

What are these foods?

1. Durian   2. Papaya   3. Rambutan

Animals of Thailand

Can you identify the animals hidden in the rainforest? There are six hidden.

_____
_____
_____
_____
_____
_____

Popular Pastimes

Find the answers to the following questions.

1. What are these two men doing?   _____
2. This is called   _____.
3. Do women participate in this sport?   _____
4. How does Thai boxing differ from western-style boxing?
   _____
5. What are these women doing?   _____
6. What special costumes are they wearing?   _____
7. Their _____ movements are ver y flexible.
8. How do the Thai dancers differ from western-style dancers?
   _____

THAILAND

Trade in Thailand - Exports and Imports
Name the main exports and imports in Thailand.

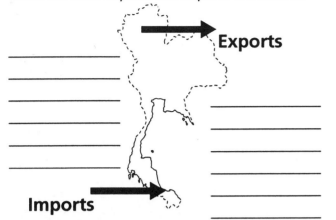

Exports

_____
_____
_____   _____
_____   _____
_____   _____
                             _____
Imports   _____

Thai Handicrafts
Write a little about each of these handicrafts.

Umbrella painting - _____

Basketr y - _____
_____

Wood carving - _____
_____

Lacquerware - _____
_____

Ceramics - _____
_____

Clothing in Thailand
There are many different styles of clothing worn in Thailand.

1. _____
_____

2. _____
_____
_____
_____

What sort of people might be wearing these clothes?

3. _____
_____
_____

4. _____
_____
_____

Kite Flying
Kite flying and kite fighting are popular sports in Thailand.

• *Colour this design and draw one of your own.*

Orchids
The or chid is Thailand' s national flower . The lotus flower is popular and symbolises purity and perfection.

• *Draw an orchid and lotus flower.*

Silkworms
➡ *What do they eat?*
➡ *Draw the life cycle of a silkworm.*
➡ *How is the silk extracted?*
➡ *What is it made into?*

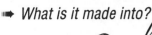

➡ *Silkworms produce the silk to make beautiful Thai silk.*

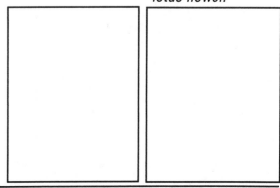

ITALY

About Italy

Italy is known as the B _ _ _ ,
because of the shape of the country.
The Italian people are friendly.
They love to t _ _ _ _ and l _ _ _ _ _ .
Their f _ _ _ _ _ is important to them.
They love company and to share good
w _ _ _ , good c _ _ _ _ _ _ such
as m _ _ _ _ _ _ _ _ _ and
r _ _ _ _ and coffees like
c _ _ _ _ _ _ _ _ _ and
e _ _ _ _ _ _ .

Italy is a fascinating country to visit.
Give three reasons why.

1. _____
2. _____
3. _____

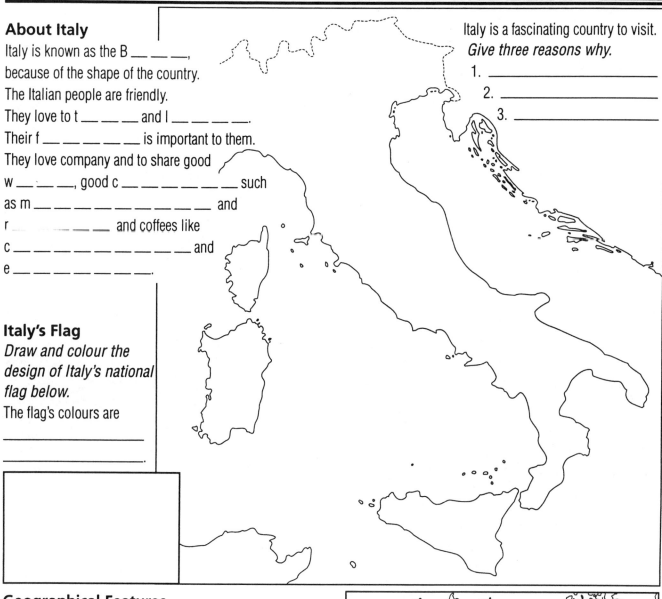

Italy's Flag

Draw and colour the design of Italy's national flag below.

The flag's colours are

_____

_____ .

Geographical Features

Use your atlas to locate and place the following on your map.

1. Sassari
2. Lake Garda
3. The Alps
4. Mount Vesuvius
5. Gulf of Taranto
6. Tiber River
7. Tyrrhenian Sea
8. Lake Como
9. Milan
10. Naples
11. Rome
12. Sardinia
13. Po River
14. San Marino
15. Pisa
16. Venice
17. Adriatic Sea
18. Sicily
19. Palermo
20. Florence
21. Taranto
22. Tuscany
23. Gulf of Salerno
24. Vatican City
25. Apennines

Where in the world is Italy? Colour it!

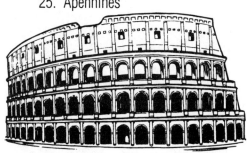

This famous building is the C _____ ,
found in the city of R _____ .
It was used for g _____ sports.

➡ *Design a travel brochure to encourage tourists to visit one of these destinations.*

ITALY

Information Search *Find the following facts about Italy.*
Population: _____
Currency: _____
Language(s) spoken: _____
Capital city: _____
Type of government: _____
Leader's title: _____
Religious beliefs: _____
Popular sports and pastimes: _____

What is
the name of
this little old lady who gives
out presents at Christmas?

_____

Spectacular Sights

Italy has some beautiful and magnificent sights to see. *Find out a little about each of the following.*

1. This is the L _____ T _____ of P_____.
Why does it lean? _____
_____
_____

2.

This is St P_____'s Church in the V _____
City, which is the home of the Pope.
Name two other sights in this tiny state.
_____
_____

3.

The statue of R _____ and R _____ is on
C _____ H _____.
They founded Rome and were suckled by a w _____ in 753 BC.

4.

Famous Italians *Research to find out why these Italians are famous.*

Name	Famous for...
Leonardo da Vinci	
Mussolini	
Sophia Loren	
Michelangelo	
Galileo Galilei	
Marco Polo	
Giovanni Casanova	
Guglielmo Marconi	
Giacomo Puccini	

The T_____ Fountain is
in R _____.
What is the legend about coins in
the fountain? _____
_____
_____

➡ *Choose one of these famous Italians and complete a profile of his/her life.*

ITALY

Italy's Gifts to the World *Find all these special Italian products which are hidden in the sleuth.*

R	O	I	M	L	D	G	O	N	D	O	L	A	D	E
E	F	T	R	T	A	I	F	M	G	L	R	B	C	A
D	E	A	E	T	V	M	C	H	E	E	S	E	S	N
I	R	L	H	E	I	N	B	J	P	O	E	I	A	O
L	R	E	T	W	D	Y	A	O	T	F	L	I	P	I
G	A	G	A	I	N	I	A	N	R	A	R	L	A	H
K	R	V	E	N	E	T	I	A	N	G	L	A	S	S
B	I	D	L	E	W	C	R	O	I	O	H	H	T	A
				I	M	D	B	J	E	I	A	F		
				R	E	P	P	I	L	F	N	E		
				N	P	I	Z	Z	A	M	V	I		
				T	E	L	E	S	C	O	P	E		

opera
fashion
telescope
David
Mona Lisa
flipper
Venetian glass
glider
cheeses
Lamborghini

Fiat
pasta
wine
Ferrari
gelati
pizza
leather
gondola

➡ *Cross out the words as you find them.*
➡ *Circle the unfamiliar words and find their meaning.*

Italian Foods
We may think of Italian foods as mainly spaghetti and pizza, but the foods are varied.
Find out about the following delicious foods.

Make a list of pasta varieties.
_____
_____
_____

Describe:
Cassata _____

Gelati _____

Sauces for pasta
Bolognaise _____

Carbonara _____
_____

Marinara _____
_____

What toppings are put on a pizza? _____
_____

What are these foods?
Minestrone _____

Antipasto _____
_____

Polenta _____
_____

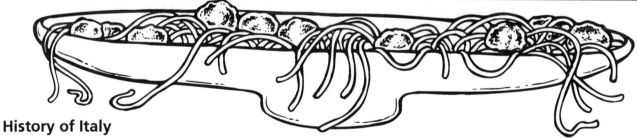

History of Italy
Highlight the key words in the following passage about Etruscans.
The Etruscans first came to Italy by sea from the Middle East more than 2 800 years ago. They settled in an area which is now called Tuscany. Paintings, household objects and terracotta figures have been found in Etruscan tombs.
These show that the Etruscans loved dancing, music, feasting and games. It is thought that the Etruscans introduced the olive, the wine grape and the chariot to Italy. The arch was first designed by Etruscan architects. The Etruscans lived in temples made of stone and wood decorated with terracotta ornaments and statues.
Key Point 1: _____
Key Point 2: _____
Key Point 3: _____

ITALY

Trade in Italy - Exports and Imports

Exports

_____
_____
_____
_____
_____

Imports ➤

_____
_____
_____
_____

Did you know?

It is good luck to eat gnocchi
on 29 September.
What are gnocchi?

_____

Find out why it is good luck.

Pompeii

What is the name of the mountain which erupted and
completely buried the city of Pompeii?

_____

When? _____
The city was covered in _____, but
was excavated 1 600 years after the eruption. What was
found? _____
_____

Name one other active volcano. _____

Vatican City

➡ *Complete a mini-report about Vatican
City. You need to include:*

1. Size of the State
2. Location
3. Population
4. Head of State
5. Main Buildings
6. Plan of buildings in State with labels.
7. Precious works of art in the Vatican

➡ *You may present your report in written
form, booklet, chart or as a class talk.*

A Special Place - Venice

Venice is one of the most beautiful cities in the world.
What feature makes it different from other cities?

_____

Instead of streets, there are _____
with bridges connecting the buildings.
What is a gondola? _____
Venice is in danger of sinking. Fumes and salt air are
eating into the foundations of buildings.
Vibrations from motor boats are eroding the
foundations as well.

➡ *Suggest a solution to this environmental
problem.* _____
_____
_____
_____
_____

Paintings

Leonardo da Vinci painted the famous Mona Lisa.
Choose a person, draw a portrait of him/her in the frame.

SCANDINAVIA

About Scandinavia

Generally, Scandinavia is used to describe the countries

of N _ _ _ _ _ _, S _ _ _ _ _ _, and

D _ _ _ _ _ _ _. The Scandinavian countries,

F _ _ _ _ _ _ _ and I _ _ _ _ _ _

may also be called the N _ _ _ _ _

countries.

Scandinavian Pine

The Vikings believed that trees supported

the universe. In fact, that was probably

true, because their land was covered

with forests of trees, which they

used in many ways.

Can you think of examples

for these uses of trees?

Furniture - _____

_____

Foods - _____

_____

Medicines - _____

_____

Fuel - _____

_____

Housing - _____

_____

Geographical Features

Use your atlas to locate and place the following on

your map.

1. Arctic Circle
2. Norwegian Sea
3. Atlantic Ocean
4. Jutland Peninsula
5. Copenhagen
6. Barents Sea
7. Gulf of Bothnia
8. Lapland
9. Baltic Sea
10. Stockholm
11. Helsinki
12. Lake Vänern
13. Bergen
14. Narvik

15. Oslo
16. Turku
17. Odense
18. North Sea
19. Vaasa
20. Lulea

Where in the world is Scandinavia? Colour it!

Scandinavian People

The typical features of Scandinavians

are their blonde hair and blue eyes.

• *Colour this costume in*

bright colours.

➥ *Father Christmas has his workshop in which Nordic country?* _____

SCANDINAVIA

Information Search *Find the following facts about the countries of Scandinavia.*

NORWAY
People of Norway are called _____.
Population: _____
Capital city: _____
Currency: _____
Religious beliefs: _____
Type of government: _____

Trade in Norway
Exports - _____
_____
Imports - _____
_____

NORWAY'S FLAG DESIGN

DENMARK'S FLAG DESIGN

SWEDEN
People of Sweden are called _____.
Population: _____
Capital city: _____
Currency: _____
Religious beliefs: _____
Type of government: _____

Trade in Sweden
Exports - _____
Imports - _____

DENMARK
People of Denmark are called _____.
Population: _____
Capital city: _____ Currency: _____
Religious beliefs: _____
Type of government: _____

Trade in Sweden
Exports - _____
Imports - _____

Runes
What are the Rune Stones?
_____
_____

The Vikings *Answer the following questions on the back of this sheet.*
1. From which countries did the Vikings originate?
2. How did the families of the Vikings live?
3. Describe some Viking foods.
4. What did the Vikings use the plentiful trees for?
5. Why did the Viking's sail to other countries? Which countries?
6. What does it mean - 'Vikings were raiders and traders'?
7. Draw some shields and swords of a Viking warrior.
8. Who was Eric the Red?
9. Draw a picture of a Viking.
10. Why was 'Thor' important to the Vikings?
11. Would you have wanted to be a Viking? Why?
➡ *Use your answers to make up an Information Sheet about these fascinating people.*

Viking Ships
The Vikings designed and built ships called
L_____.
they were light and strong.
The striped sails were
r_____ and
w_____.
➡ *Can you construct a model of a Viking ship?*

SCANDINAVIA

Scandinavian Climate

The Scandinavian countries are close to the North Pole and the Arctic Circle.

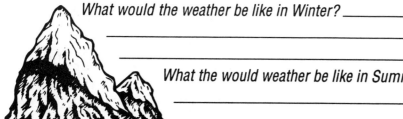

What would the weather be like in Winter? _____

_____

What the would weather be like in Summer? _____

_____

Flora and Fauna of Scandinavia

Can you find these words in the sleuth?

Flora

In the south of Scandinavia there are many trees, and most of the land is covered in deep forests. Towards the north, the vegetation is sparse because of the cold toward the Arctic Circle.

willow   pine
fir   heather
spruce   oak
elm   beech

R	O	P	A	D	E	O	U	S	I	P	O	O	T
E	R	U	I	N	U	A	M	S	P	G	W	A	N
R	V	F	O	**N**	R	D	E	I	R	R	I	K	D
P	C	F	L	N	E	B	W	S	**E**	O	U	M	P
O	N	**I**	K	O	T	H	I	H	H	U	R	C	N
L	Y	N	X	M	T	A	L	W	T	S	E	B	E
A	E	L	O	L	O	**R**	L	E	A	E	O	**E**	S
R	D	M	F	A	I	E	O	R	E	N	I	E	E
B	T	Y	M	S	C	S	W	U	H	H	T	C	
E	C	T	R	I	E	O	E	O	T	S	B	H	
A	S	O	A	S	N	P	L	H	L	K	E	E	
R	E	E	**D**	E	T	G	M	T	P	F	I	**R**	

Fauna

fox   otter
cod   lemming
grouse   wolf
deer   lynx
puffin   hares
trout   salmon
polar bear

Put a circle around the two endangered animals.

➡ *Unjumble the letters in bold print to find the name of an animal associated with Christmas.* _____

Scandinavian Foods

Describe these foods.

Blue vein cheese - _____

_____

Herring - _____

Smorgasbord - _____

_____

Havarti - _____

Danish pastries - _____

Meatballs - _____

Fiskekaker - _____

Smørrebrød - _____

_____

➡ *Using some of the foods eaten in Scandinavia, write out a menu for a typical Scandinavian meal on the chart on the right.*

MENU

SCANDINAVIA

Lapland

Look in resource books to find the answers to the following questions.

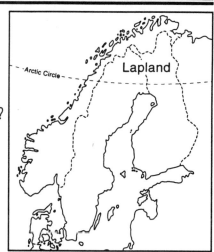

Arctic Circle — Lapland

1. What direction is Lapland from the Scandinavian countries? _____
2. By what name are the Laplanders often called? _____
3. What animal is herded by the Laps? _____
4. This animal is used for _____.
5. Do the Laplanders live a simple life? _____
   How do you know this? _____
   _____
6. What form of transport do they use? _____

Did you know?

What and where are the Tivoli Gardens?

_____

_____

_____

What is a fjord?

_____

_____

Which Scandinavian country claims Greenland as its own?

_____

_____

What famous product is made by Orrefors and Kosta Boda?

_____

_____

Who was Leif Ericsson's father?

_____

_____

Who invented skis?

_____

_____

Winter Collage

Using the picture below as a guide, design a Winter picture.

• *Cut out coloured pieces of paper in the shape of your design and glue them on. (Think of ice, snow, reflections!)*

People Profiles

Why are these Scandinavians famous?

Hans Christian Anderson

Nationality: _____

Famous for _____

_____

Alfred Nobel

Nationality: _____

Famous for _____

_____

Bjorn Borg, Mats Wilander, Stefan Edberg

Nationalities: _____

Famous for _____

_____

Leif Ericsson

Nationality: _____

Famous for _____

_____

World Map

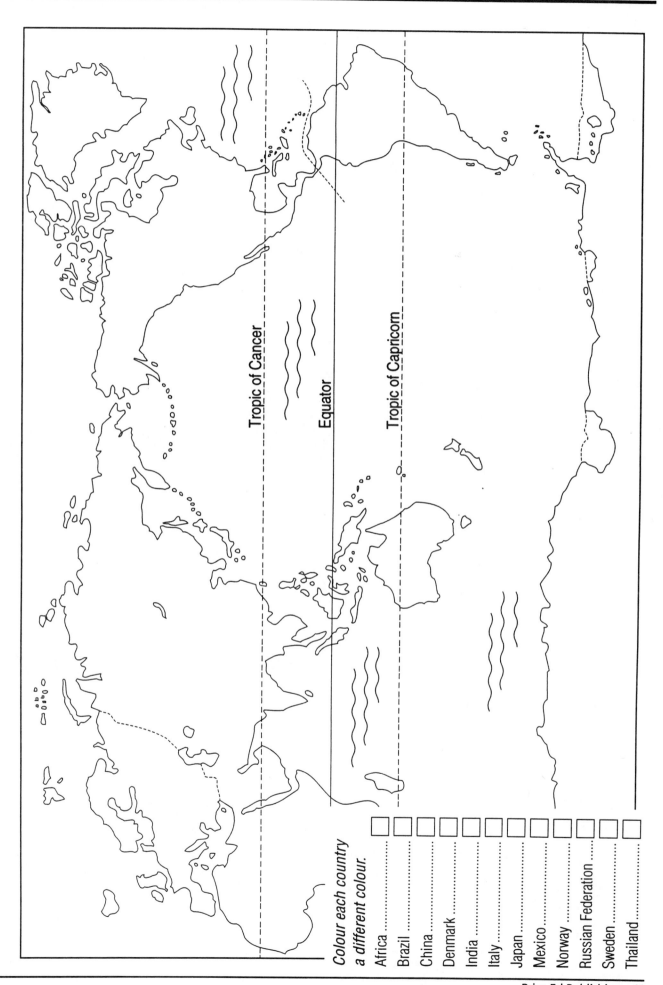

Tropic of Cancer

Equator

Tropic of Capricorn

*Colour each country
a different colour.*

Africa ....

Brazil ....

China ....

Denmark ....

India ....

Italy ....

Japan ....

Mexico ....

Norway ....

Russian Federation ....

Sweden ....

Thailand ....

Individual Nation Review

This nation/country is _____.

It is part of the continent of _____, and is surrounded by the _____ ocean(s).

Its capital city is _____. Once I arrived in this nation, I would travel by _____.

I would eat _____

_____

because it tastes _____

_____

_____ and looks like this.

Here's me on a _____

I would need to wear _____

_____

because the weather is _____

_____

_____

There are so many exciting and spectacular places to visit, but I would take a photo of _____

_____

_____

to remember this place!

Here's me wearing a traditional costume.

Here's me visiting _____

I would buy these souvenirs _____

_____

_____

_____

_____

I would recommend a visit to _____ because _____

_____

_____

_____

Nation	Population	Capital city	Language(s)	Currency	Religious beliefs	Popular sports and pastimes	Foods	Trade		Spectacular sights
								Exports	Imports	
CHINA										
AFRICA										
RUSSIAN FEDERATION										
INDIA										
MEXICO										
JAPAN										
BRAZIL										
THAILAND										
ITALY										
NORWAY										
SWEDEN										
DENMARK										
SCANDINAVIA										

Answers

Answers accurate to January 1997.
Some historical dates and spellings
may vary slightly according to
resources used.

CHINA 1 - 4

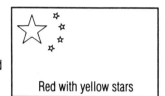

Red with yellow stars

About China - *Missing Words* -
Oldest, world, people, population,
country, empire.
The Willow Pattern - is a blue and
white design which tells the legend
of a young Chinese couple.
Building - The Forbidden City in front of Tiananmen Square in Beijing.
China's Neighbours - Mongolia, Russia, North Korea, Vietnam, Laos,
India, Bhutan, Nepal, Pakistan, Myanmar, Tajikistan, Kyrgyz,
Kazakhstan, Afghanistan.
Information Search - *Population*: 1 218 000 000 in 1997, *Currency*:
Yuan, *Language(s) spoken*: Chinese, *Capital city*: Beijing, *Type of
government*: Communist, *Leader's title*: President, *Religious beliefs*:
Confucianism, Taoism and Buddhism, *Popular sports and pastimes*:
martial arts, taijiquan and basketball.
Picture - Abacus.
History of China - 1. Ancient Chinese people 2. To keep out invaders
from Central Asia 3. No 4. A Terracotta Army of more than 7 000 life-
size men and horses 5. Italian explorer who came to China overland
following the silk trading routes 6. A Chinese philosopher 7. High
moral standards, well-ordered society, respect for ancestors and the
past 8. Religious leader from Tibet
Historical Dates - 551 BC: Birth of Confucius, 221-206 BC: Chin (or
Qin) people formed the first empire, 202 BC-AD 220: Han Dynasty,
AD 581-618: Sui Dynasty, AD 618-907: Tang Dynasty, AD 960-1279:
Song Dynasty, AD 1279-1368: Mongols invade, and set up the Yuan
Dynasty, AD 1368-1644: Ming Dynasty, AD 1644-1912: Manchurians
invade, and set up Qing Dynasty, AD 1920s: Communist Party formed.
A Dynasty is a series of rulers coming from the same family.
Communism is when all work and property is shared by the
community.
Chinese Inventions - compass, wheelbarrow, gunpowder, kites,
porcelain Answer - paper
Even More Inventions! - rudder, fireworks, silk, umbrella, guns
Chinese Foods - *Missing Words* - north, noodles, rice, scarce,
shoots, bean, soya, steamed, baskets, woks, tea, bowls, chopsticks,
dairy, cheese
Animals of China - Panda, World Wide, Nature, bamboo, Siberian,
deer, monkeys, cranes, peacocks, Mandarin.
Trade in China - *Exports* - Oil, clothing, textiles, tea, fruit
Imports - machinery, iron, steel, grain, chemicals, vehicles.
Yin and Yang - *Yin*: female, dark, cold, feminine, passive, yielding,
good. *Yang*: male, bright, hot, masculine, active, assertive, evil.
Chinese Festivals - Answers will vary.
The Yellow River - 1. Huang He 2. Soil drains into the river making
it yellow-brown 3. Junk 4. Transport and accommodation 5. flat

AFRICA 5 - 8

About Africa - *Missing Words* - Sahara Desert, Nile River.
Capital Cities - *Egypt*: Cairo, *Somalia*: Mogadishu, *South Africa*: Cape
Town, *Sudan*: Khartoum, *Libya*: Tripoli, *Morocco*: Rabat, *Nigeria*:
Lagos, *Kenya*: Nairobi.
Building - The shapes above are the Pyramids of Egypt.

Spectacular Sights - *Victoria Falls*: Zambia and Zimbabwe, *The
Sphinx*: Egypt, *Mt Kilamanjaro*: Tanzania.
Information Search - Answers may vary according to nation chosen.
The People of Africa - Answers may vary.
The Differences Between Races -
Masai warrior: *Appearance*: Tall, slender, very dark skin. *Dress*: One
piece cloth wrapped around body. *Foods*: Milk, meat, grains, berries.
Housing: Mud houses. *Transport*: Generally walking. *Language*: Maa
(Nilo-Saharan). *Religion*: Not known.
Saudi Arabian: *Appearance*: Short/slight, dark complexion. *Dress*:
Long cotton garment (thawb) head covering (ghutra). *Foods*: Dairy
products, dates, lamb, rice, fruit, vegetables. *Housing*: Stone or mud
houses in villages. *Transport*: Camels in the desert areas. *Language*:
Arabic. *Religion*: Islamic.
Wild Animals of Africa - cheetah, gorilla, rhinoceros, elephant,
okapi, jackal, lion, ibis, ape, chimpanzee, gnu, gazelle/giraffe,
flamingo, crocodile, hyena, giraffe/gazelle.
African Foods - rural, food, soil, keep, goats, peanuts, drier, rice,
root, north, common, vegetables, flat, grains, coffee, coconuts, sell.
Trade in Africa - *Exports* - Petroleum, gold, diamonds, coffee, natural
gas, cocoa *Imports* - Food, machinery, iron, steel, motor vehicles
Problems in Africa - *Somalia*: country in Africa in real need of food,
medicines and clean water. *Apartheid*: a rigid system of racial
separation - voted against in Africa in recent years. *Rwanda*: country in
Africa with 1 000s of starving and sick people. *Nelson Mandela*: led
the movement which abolished Apartheid, jailed for 28 years.

RUSSIAN FEDERATION 9 - 12

| white |
| blue |
| red |

About Russia - *Missing Words* -
Poetry, music, ballet, literature,
painting
Building - Saint Basil's Cathedral in
Moscow.
Perestroika - means reforms,
rebuilding and restructuring.
Glasnost - means freedom to speak out, openness.
The picture is of Peter the Great.
Information Search - *Population*: 147 500 000 in 1997, *Currency*:
Ruble, *Main language(s) spoken*: Russian, *Capital city*: Moscow, *Type
of government*: Democratic, *Leader's title*: President, *Religious beliefs*:
Orthodox, Muslims/Islam, *Popular sports and pastimes*: soccer,
basketball, ice-hockey, ballet.
Building - The Winter Palace in Leningrad, now Hermitage Museum.
History of Russia - 1547-1584: The first Russian Tsar was Ivan the
Terrible, 1682-1725: Peter the Great ruled, 1762-1796: Catherine the
Great ruled, 1917: The Bolshevik Party, led by Vladmir Lenin, seized
power, 1922: Formation of the USSR, 1924-1953: Joseph Stalin ruled,
1985: Mikhail Gorbachev becomes leader of the Communist Party,
1991: Russia is formed and led by Boris Yeltsin.
The Russian Language - Cyrillic, ninth.
Famous Russians - *Anna Pavlova*: one the greatest female ballet
dancers, *Yuri Gagarin*: the first human in space, *Mikhail Sholokhov*: won
the Nobel Prize in 1965, *Anton Chekhoz*: wrote short stories and plays,
Grigori Rasputin: believed he could heal the Tsar's sick son, *Olga Korbut*:
won three Olympic Gold Medals for gymnastics, *Rudolph Nureyev*: one of
the greatest male ballet dancers, *Alexander Solzhenitsyn*: wrote about the
horrors of prison camps set up by Stalin, won the Nobel Peace prize for
literature in 1970, *Peter Tchaikovsky*: musical composer of The Nutcracker
and Swan Lake, *Leo Tolstoy*: author of War and Peace.

Animals of Russia - The letters are WORBERBAN and the unjumbled answer is Brown Bear.

Russian Foods - *Vodka* is a famous Russian drink originally made from wheat, but now made from potatoes, corn and other cereals. *Shashlik* is cooked meat along a stick. *Blinis* are pancakes, *Kasha* is a kind of gruel or thin porridge, *Borshch* is beetroot soup. *Caviar* is fish eggs, *Samovar* is a large container used to heat tea, *Beef Stroganov* is beef stew with mushrooms and sour cream sauce.

Traditions of Russia - *Grandfather Frost*: comes once every year in the New Year and he brings presents for everyone.

Bolshoi Ballet: is known for its brilliance in technique and rigorous movements. Some famous ballet dancers are Nureyev, Nijinsky and Baryshnikov.

Moscow Circus: one of the greatest circuses on Earth. Performing animals are bears, horses and lions, other acts include clowns, trapeze artists, lion taming and dancing bears.

The Elixir of Youth - The secret recipe: lemon and garlic.

INDIA   13 - 16

About India - *Missing Words* -
Population, largest, simple, crowded, history, religion, colours, flowers, wildlife, many, customs, mountains, rainforests, deserts.

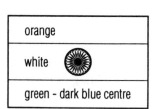

orange	
white	
green - dark blue centre	

Mountain Range - The Himalayas in the north of India, the highest mountain in the world is Mt Everest.

Information Search - *Population*: 930 000 000 in 1997, *Currency*: Rupee, *Language(s) spoken*: Hindu, English, *Capital city*: New Delhi, *Type of government*: Democratic, *Leader's title*: President and Prime Minister, *Religious beliefs*: Hindu and Muslim, *Popular sports and pastimes*: hockey, cricket and soccer.

Religion in India and The Ganges River - 1. Chicken, pork and lamb 2. Do not swallow any water 3. Provide other places to bathe and for the disposal of rubbish and waste

The Taj Mahal - 1. Taj Mahal 2. Emperor Shah Jahan 3. In memory of his wife Mumtaz Mahal 4. Started in 1632 and finished in 1653 5. Teacher check.

Clothing in India - *Sari*: straight piece of cloth draped around the body as a long dress. *Dhoti*: white garment wrapped between the legs. *Turban*: long scarf wrapped around the head. *Lunghi*: cloth wrapped around the waist worn by women.

Indian Foods and Drink - 1. rice 2. beef 3. ginger, tumeric, garlic, coriander, cloves 4. chapattis 5. tandoor 6. true 7. north, south 8. knife and fork, rolled with their fingers 9. right.
Samosa: deep-fried pastries filled with potatoes. *Pappadums*: flat bread. *Dhal*: porridge made with softened beans. *Korma*: type of meat dish made with spices and yoghurt.

Indian Animals and Birds - falcon, grey wolf, camels, peacock, tiger, buffalo, king cobra, flamingo, bears, red panda, rhinoceros, leopard, monkey, elephant. *Elephant differences*: The trunk and ears.

Trade in India - *Exports* - clothing, textiles, diamonds, tea, handicrafts, iron ore, machinery *Imports* - petrol, fertilizer, transportation equipment, non-electrical machinery, grains, edible oils.

Transport in India - *Cities*: trains, buses, bikes and cars
Country areas: camels in the desert, bullock carts.

The Golden Temple - located in Amritsar, Sikh religion, feature: holiest shrine painted gold and built by the Sikhs.

MEXICO   17 - 20

About Mexico - *Missing Words* -
United Mexican States
Mexico's Flag - green, white and red.
Picture - The Great Pyramid at Chichen Itza.
Monarch Butterfly - orange, black, red, yellow and white.

green	white	red

Other migrating birds/animals: Answers may vary.
Spectacular Sights - *Acapulco*: Beautiful beaches, cliff faces, *Yucatan Peninsula*: Ruins of Aztec civilisations, *Popocatepett Volcano*: highest peak in North America covered in snow, surrounded by sugar cane fields.

Information Search - *Population*: 93 700 000 in 1997, *Currency*: Peso, *Language(s) spoken*: Spanish, *Capital city*: Mexico City, *Type of government*: Democracy, *Leader's title*: President, *Religious beliefs*: Roman Catholic, *Popular sports and pastimes*: soccer and bullfighting.
Plant - This is a cactus plant.

History of Mexico - AD 250, Mid 1300s, 1519-1527, 1821-1824, 1846-1848, 1863, 1929-1934.

Mexican Foods - enchilada, tostada, burrito, avocado, salsa, taco, tortilla, chilli, frijoles, cheese, guacamole, biscochos, tamale, nachos, cacao, tequila, beans, vanilla, coffee, mole.
Tortilla: a thin flat corn-meal bread shaped by hand or machine, cooked on an ungreased griddle. *Biscochos*: a Mexican biscuit *Guacamole*: a dip made with avocado and chilli. *Tequila*: is an alcoholic drink made from the maguey plant.

Flora and Fauna of Mexico - 1. orchids, damp 2. cactus, water, roots, rain 3. Grey, born, warm, weigh, milk 4. lizard, monster, scales, painful, rocky 5. monkey, loudest, forests.

Trade in Mexico - zinc, lead and copper *Silver Products* - jewellery, ornaments and tableware *Exports* - petrol, oil, copper, salt, silver, zinc, engines, coffee, fruit and vegetables *Imports* - machinery, electrical goods and motor vehicles

Mexican Clothing - *Sombrero*: a hat with a very large brim
Poncho: a cloak made of cloth with a hole for the head.

Mexican Festivals - *Fiesta*: carnivals or festivals with fireworks
Pinata: a earthenware or paper maché animal shape filled with sweets and toys, it is hung and children break it with a stick to get the sweets.
Siesta: an afternoon nap

Japan   21 - 24

Climate in Japan - *Missing Words* -
north, cold, Summers, humid, danger, winds, rains, Spring.
Japan's Flag - red, white.
Geographical Features -
1. Hokkaido, Honshu, Kyushu and
Shikoku 2. Tokyo 3. North Korea, South Korea, Russia, China
4. Hokkaido 5. Honshu 6. Kyushu 7. Honshu 8. Hokkaido
9. Honshu 10. Honshu 11. Honshu

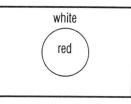

Mountain - This is Mt Fuji. Height - 3 776 m.

Information Search - *Population*: 125 000 030 in 1997, *Currency*: Yen, *Language(s) spoken*: Japanese, *Capital city*: Tokyo, *Type of government*: Parliamentary Democracy, *Leader's title*: Prime Minister, *Religious beliefs*: Buddhism and Shinto, *Popular sports and pastimes*: baseball, sumo wrestling, golf and table tennis.

Japanese Writing - *Differences* - Written in columns not in rows, and

written from right to left not left to right.

Japanese Foods - Japanese, rice, raw, fresh, famous, fish, sushi, seaweed, snack.

About Japan - *Crossword One Clues* - 1. shrine 2. buddhism 3. rice 4. kimono 5. judo 6. karate 7. sushi. The island is Shikoku.

Crossword Two Clues - 1. cherry 2. origami 3. shinkansen 4. fish 5. haiku 6. sumo. The island is Honshu.

Trade in Japan - *Exports* - cars, electrical appliances, iron, steel and office machinery *Imports* - petrol, ores, timber, coal, grain and meat

Japanese Brand Names - Toyota, Honda, Nissan, Sony, Panasonic, Mazda and Hitachi

Japanese Words - *Samurai*: A traditional Japanese warrior *Tatami*: the traditional rice straw mat *Kabuki*: the traditional Japanese plays *Sake*: Japanese rice wine

BRAZIL 25 - 28

About Brazil - *Missing Words* - Portuguese, Indians, West Africa.

Brazil's Name - Brazil got its name from the Brazil wood which is a hard redwood found in South America.

Brazil's Flag - green, yellow, light blue and white.

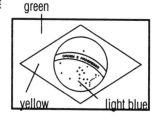
green / yellow / light blue

Building - is the Crown of Thorns Cathedral in Brasilia.

Brazil's Neighbours - Uruguay, Argentina, Paraguay, Bolivia, Peru, Columbia, Venezuela, Guyana, Surinam and French Guiana.

Information Search - *Population*: 160 757 000 in 1997, *Currency*: Cruzado/Cruziero, *Language(s) spoken*: Portuguese, *Capital city*: Brasilia, *Religious beliefs*: Roman Catholic, *Type of government*: Federal Republic, *Leader's title*: President, *Popular sports and pastimes*: water sports, soccer and car racing.

The statue is the Statue of Christ overlooking Rio de Janeiro.

Brazilian Products - *Coffee Beans*: are grown, dried, roasted and then ground. *Brazil Nut*: cashew, peanuts, bananas, oranges, pineapples, papaya and lemons. *Timber*: furniture, houses, plywood, charcoal. *Cacao Beans*: chocolate. The beans are dried, cleaned and roasted, then ground and blended to make cocoa. *The Rubber Tree*: the trunk is cut on an angle, the sap drips out and is collected in containers, then made into tyres and rubber products.

Brazilian Wildlife - hummingbird, toucans, electric eel, macaw, anaconda, sloth, tapir and alligator.

Brazilian Festivals and Carnivals - *Key Points* - 1. The largest carnival is in Rio de Janeiro. 2. Festivals are full of parties, dancing and music. 3. Colourful floats and costumes everywhere. 4. Many different races have influenced the music and dance.

Brazilian Foods and Drink - *Mandioca*: root vegetables, *Manioc*: starchy root (cassava), *Feijoada*: national dish - blackbeans, dried beef and pork, *Beverages*: coffee, batidas - fruit beverage with rum, maté (tea), seafoods - crabs, shrimp, lobster.

Trade in Brazil - *Exports* - cars, oranges, orange juice, soya beans and coffee *Imports* - chemicals, fertilizer, machinery and wheat *Missing Words* - warm, wet, fish, sugar cane and soya beans.

Sports and Leisure - Missing Words - soccer, futebol, Pele, car race, Ayrton Senna.

World Cup Soccer - 1958, 1962, 1970 and 1994.

Music and Dance - Spanish, African, Indian, North American. *Dances* - Samba, Lambada and Bossa Nova. *Instruments* - Maraca, Viola, Pife and Tamborim.

THAILAND 29 - 52

About Thailand - *Missing Words* - 'Land of Smiles' or 'Land of the Free'.

Thailand's Flag - red, blue and white.

Statue - Buddha is at Wat Mahathat, one of many temples in Bangkok.

red
white
blue
white
red

Buddha, Buddhism and Buddhist temples - 1. *Buddha* is the name given to the founder of Buddhism. It means 'enlightened' or 'awakened' one. He lived more than 2 000 years ago. 3. Buddhists believe in rebirth.

Information Search - *Population*: 60 271 000 in 1997, *Currency*: baht, *Language(s) spoken*: Thai, *Capital city*: Bangkok, *Type of government*: Constitutional Monarchy, *Leader's title*: Prime Minister, *Religious beliefs*: Buddhism, *Popular sports and pastimes*: soccer and kick-boxing.

History of Thailand - *Missing Words* - 1. Father of Thailand, Thailand, 1299. 2. Alphabet, ceramic crafts, arts learned. 3. Chao Phraya River, Burmese, Bangkok. 4. Siam, 1939.

Transport throughout Thailand - 1. Chao Phraya River 2. Klongs 3. Ferries, taxis, vans, motorbikes, cars, buses. 4. Wooden boats, carts. 5. Left 6. Four 7. Tuk-tuks and cycle rickshaws. 8. Teacher check.

Seasons in Thailand - Hot dry Spring, hot wet Summer, a mild Winter.

Thai Foods - *Unjumble* - pepper, ginger, chilli, coriander, mint, basil. *Sleuth* - garlic, durian, noodles, rice, coconut milk, crabs, vegetables, fish, prawns, spices. *Durian*: oval fruit, very smelly, spiny rind but pleasant taste. *Papaya (pawpaw)*: yellow, sweet pulp with black seeds. *Rambutan*: bright red fruit covered in hairs.

Animals of Thailand - elephant, monkey, snake, eagle, water buffalo, spiders, moths.

Popular Pastimes - 1. Fighting 2. Kick-boxing or Thai-boxing 3. No 4. Rules allow men to kick above the waist 5. Dancing 6. Woven silk with gold, very elaborate 7. Hand 8. Slower more detailed and intricate movements which tell a story or legend.

Trade in Thailand - *Exports* - rice, textiles, rubber and fish *Imports* - oil products, foods, machinery and manufactured foods

Thai Handicrafts - *Umbrella painting*: is done by hand. Designs are hand painted. *Basketry*: Baskets, furniture and ornaments are woven using cane. *Wood carving*: Ornaments, bowls are carved from wood. *Lacquerware*: boxes, bowls are painted and lacquered usually in dark colours. *Ceramics*: pottery and ornaments are crafted and painted.

Clothing in Thailand - 1. Rice planter 2. Buddhist monk 3. Thai dancer 4. Rural worker .

Silkworms - *Silkworms eat*: mulberry leaves *How Silk is extracted*: the threads of silk are reeled from the cocoon of the dead pupa - several at a time, to strengthen the thread. The silk is twisted into coiled bundles.

Silk is made into: the silk is dyed and woven on looms to make clothing and materials.

ITALY 33 - 36

About Italy - *Missing Words* - boot, talk, laugh, family, wine, cheeses, mozzarella, romano, cappuccino, espresso.

Italy's Flag - green, white and red.

Building - The famous building is the

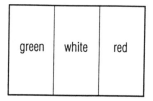

green	white	red

Colosseum in Rome, used for Gladiator Sports.

Information Search - *Population:* 58 262 000 in 1997, *Currency:* Lira, *Language(s) spoken:* Italian, *Capital city:* Rome, *Religious beliefs:* Roman Catholic, *Type of government:* Parliamentary Democracy, *Leader's title:* President, *Popular sports and pastimes:* soccer and basketball.

Little Old Lady - La Befana.

Spectacular Sights - 1. Leaning Tower of Pisa, it was built on unstable soil, began to lean after the third storey was built. 2. St Peter's Church in Vatican City, Papal Gardens, Sistene Chapel. 3. Rhomulus and Remus, Capitoline Hill, wolf. 4. Trevi Fountain in Rome, if you throw a coin into the fountain, you will return to Italy.

Famous Italians - Leonardo da Vinci: Great artist who painted the Mona Lisa. Mussolini: cruel dictator in Italy for 21 years. Sophia Loren: A movie star. Michelangelo: Sculptor and artist who painted the ceiling of the Sistine Chapel. Galileo Galilei: An astronomer and physicist who invented the telescope and other inventions. Marco Polo: Explorer who followed the silk route to China. Giovanni Casanova: Adventurer and author. Guglielmo Marconi: Inventor and electrical engineer who invented the wireless radio. Giacomo Puccini: Opera composer of Madam Butterfly.

Italian Foods - *Pasta Varieties:* Spaghetti, penne, fettucine, linguine, macaroni, canneloni, tortellini and ravioli. *Cassata:* is ice-cream with nuts and fruit. *Gelati:* is an Italian dessert made of ice-cream, flavoured with fruit. *Bolognaise:* meat in a garlic and tomato sauce. *Carbonara:* ham and mushrooms in a cheese sauce. *Marinara:* a sauce with seafood. *Minestrone:* thick soup with beans, meat, vegetables and pasta. *Antipasto:* thinly sliced cold meats and cheese eaten before the meal. *Polenta:* thick porridge made from maize. *Pizza Toppings:* cheese, onions, ham, peppers, olives, anchovies, prawns, tomato, salami and many others.

History of Italy - *Key Points* - 1. Etruscans came from the Middle East and settled in Tuscany. 2. Objects found in tombs show they loved dancing, music and feasting. 3. Introduced grapes, olives and chariots and designed the first arch.

Trade in Italy - *Exports* - clothing, shoes, cars, machinery, fruit, vegetables and chemicals *Imports* - machinery, petrol, cars, textiles, yarns and metals

Did you know? - Gnocchi are made of potato.

A Special Place - Venice - It is built on over 120 islands, Canals. *A gondola:* is a long boat used to transport people through the canals.

Pompeii - Mt Vesuvius in AD 79. City covered in lava, ash and cinders. Bodies, ornaments, buildings and statues were found. *Active volcano:* Stromboli

SCANDINAVIA   37 - 40

About Scandinavia - *Missing Words* - Norway, Sweden, Denmark, Finland, Iceland, Nordic.

Father Christmas - his workshop is in Finland or in Lapland.

Information Search -

Norway - The people of Norway are called Norwegians.
Population: 4 331 000 in 1997, *Capital city:* Oslo, *Currency:* Krone *Religious beliefs:* Lutheran, *Type of government:* Monarchy

Trade in Norway - *Exports* - oil and metal
Imports - grain, iron and steel

Sweden - The people of Sweden are called Swedes.
Population: 8 822 000 in 1997, *Capital city:* Stockholm, *Currency:* Krona *Religious beliefs:* Lutheran, *Type of government:* Monarchy

Trade in Sweden - *Exports* - paper, sewing machines, crystal and cars *Imports* - fuels, farming products and chemicals

Denmark - The people of Denmark are called Danes.
Population: 5 200 000 in 1997, *Capital city:* Copenhagen, *Currency:* Krone *Religious beliefs:* Lutheran, *Type of government:* Monarchy

Trade in Denmark - *Exports* - meat and diary products *Imports* - fuels, iron and steel

Rune Stones - Viking's writings found on stone or bone, made up of mostly straight lines.

The Vikings - 1. North-west Europe, moved to Denmark, Norway and Sweden. 2. Stone or wood houses, small communities, each with chief. 3. Two meals daily, beef, cheese, eggs, milk, deer, elk and fish. 4. Houses, boats, wood carvings, weapons, shields, spears, arrows, tables, chairs. 5. Loot and take other countries. England, France, Germany, Ireland, Italy, Russia and Spain. 6.Fierce people who raided countries, eventually using them as trade routes.   7. Teacher check 8. A Norwegian who sailed with his family and hundreds of Icelanders to settle in Greenland in 985. 9. Teacher check 10. Thor was the god of thunder, lightning, rain and wind. Vikings prayed to Thor for good harvests and fortune. 11. Teacher check

Viking Ships - Longships, red, white.

Scandinavian Climate - *Winter* - very cold, freezing temperatures, ports freeze over. *Summer* - Dry and warm because the closeness to the oceans make it quite mild.

Flora and Fauna of Scandinavian - Unjumbled Letters - Reindeer

Scandinavian Foods - *Blue Vein cheese:* cheese injected with mould. *Herring:* a small salty fish. *Smorgasbord:* a platter of cold salads and meats. *Havarti:* a type of cheese. *Danish pastries:* desserts made from pastries filled with various fruits. *Meatballs:* rolled balls of meat cooked in sauce. *Fiskekaker:* fish cakes. *Smørrebørd:* buttered bread.

Lapland - 1. north 2. Sami or Saami 3. Reindeer 4. food, skins and transport 5. Yes, they grow their own food and live in huts 6. sleighs

Did you know? - *Tivoli Gardens:* is in Copenhagen and is an entertainment complex opened in 1843. *A fjord:* is a deep valley cut into the mountains by the sea. *Skis:* were invented by the Laplanders. *Greenland:* is owned by Denmark. *Leif Ericsson's father:* was Eric the Red. *Orrefors and Kosta Boda:* are crystal brands.

People Profiles - *Hans Christian Anderson:* was Danish. He wrote 168 children's stories including 'The Ugly Duckling' and 'Emperors New Clothes'. *Alfred Nobel:* was Swedish. He invented dynamite and established the Nobel Peace Prize. *Bjorn Borg, Mats Wilander, Stefan Edberg:* all Swedish tennis players. *Leif Ericsson:* was Norwegian. He sailed to and discovered North America in AD 1000.